' Let food be your medicine
and medicine be your food '
Hippocrates

First published in 1989 by,
Barbara Cousins.
Moorside Natural Healing Clinic.
177 Moorside Rd. Swinton. Manchester. M27 9LD.

British Library Catologuing-in-publication data. A catologue record for
this book is available from the British Library.

Printed by Comtec Print Ltd.
69 Folly Lane. Swinton. Manchester. M27 3DE.

ISBN 0 9526660 0 6

FOREWORD

For the past ten years I have practised nutritional therapy in my clinic in North Manchester. Although I practise other therapies, I use diet and detoxification with all my patients as I believe strongly that the way we eat has a profound influence on our health and well being.

I trained originally as a Home Economist and this training proved useful in my attempts to create interesting meals to successfully combat the Candida symptoms which I had developed. These new recipes together with the knowledge and experience I gained through treating myself helped to encourage me to train as a nutritional therapist.

From this point "Cooking Without" started to evolve as recipes and handouts were given to patients. "Cooking Without" was first printed in 1989 and since then its reputation has continued to grow. Requests for copies come from near and far and many individuals comment on how much they have benefitted from its use.

This edition contains even more recipes and updates on some of the old recipes as well as outlining my philosophy regarding nutritional therapy. This philosophy has developed over the years as I have learnt from treating myself and my patients as well as from training courses, books, other therapists and friends. I feel indebted to all those I have met over the years who have taught me so much.

I feel very grateful to my husband and family for all the help and encouragement they have given me over the last ten years. They have been the guinea pigs who have tested the recipes which didn't work as well as the ones contained in this book. Without the help of my two boys this book would never have made it onto the computer. Thanks must also go to John and Val, the proprietors of Swinton Health Foods above whose shop my clinic is situated. They are always ready with a smile and a sense of humour and have been a tremendous support.

I hope that "Cooking Without" will continue to help many more individuals who wish to take responsibility for their health and improve it for the better.

Best Wishes, Barbara.

CONTENTS

Detoxification.. 5
How blood sugar works.. 7
Putting Cooking Without into practice.............................. 9
Weight control... 10
Organising your cooking.. 10
Vegetarians... 12
Widening the range of foods consumed...............................
once health has been obtained.. 17
Suggested menus... 18
Ingredients and methods of cooking................................. 19
Breakfasts.. 25
Starters.. 37
Soups.. 45
Salads... 55
Mainly vegetarian... 65
Meat dishes... 95
Fish dishes... 105
Sauces.. 115
Baking Without.. 123
Desserts... 137
Why you should avoid wheat, dairy produce,
saturated fat, sugar, salt and yeast................................... 152
Some common health problems.. 159
Candida albicans... 159
Allergies and intolerances.. 162
M.E. and T.T.T... 163
Emotions, addictions and ill health................................... 165

INTRODUCTION TO COOKING WITHOUT

This book is about health, how to gain it and how to keep it. Be aware that health is not a mere absence of disease but a positive feeling of well being which embraces, mental, emotional and spiritual as well as physical health. This book is about the nutritional aspects of health, the dos and dont's of healthy eating because quite simply "we are what we eat". In all cases by giving the body sufficient of the nutrients it needs, it has the best opportunity to heal itself and to stay well.

DETOXIFICATION

The two main causes of health problems are toxicity and malnutrition.We are generally over fed but undernourished. If our bodies receive sufficient good quality fuel (vitamins, minerals etc) then they will be able to work efficiently and overcome any toxicity (poisons which should not be present in the body). Similarly if we receive insufficient of the correct nutrients our toxic load is allowed to overcome us and the result is illness.

WHERE DOES TOXICITY COME FROM?

In my opinion the main sources of toxicity are as follows :-
* Some toxicity in food is natural eg solanine in potatoes. Most toxicity in food is unnatural eg fungicides, pesticides, colourings, flavourings, stabilisers etc.
* Industry, smoking and exhaust fumes pollute our atmosphere.
* Our drinking water is polluted by both industry and farming as well as by chemicals used to 'cleanse' it.
* Most drugs contain toxicity, including over the counter remedies such as laxatives, painkillers and indigestion tablets and alcohol is also a poison.
* Around our homes, washing up liquid, deodorants, perfumes, cleaning liquids etc, are all chemically derived and as such are toxic substances which are absorbed to a certain extent by our bodies.
* Bottled up feelings and emotions which we have not dealt with but have suppressed constitute emotional toxicity which in turn effects our physical body.

HOW DOES TOXICITY AFFECT OUR HEALTH?

There is no way we can completely avoid toxicity and our bodies are built to cope with a certain amount; our liver being our main organ of detoxification. Toxicity is naturally removed from our bodies through the bowel, the waterworks, the outward breath and the skin. It is only when eliminating channels cannot cope with this removal that the body will use other means to eliminate toxicity or to let us know that all is not well (illness).

Often symptoms of illness are the body using its overflow system in order to remove excess toxicity. The safest place to overflow is through the skin as this is farthest away from the vital organs and enables toxicity to be removed to the outside world. Years ago individuals used to do a lot of elimination through the skin and history books always talk about boils and carbuncles. Nowadays these are less common and few individuals eliminate well through the skin. Even those teenagers who live on mars bars and chips frequently have good complexions. Eliminating through the skin causes health problems such as psoriasis, eczema, rashes, itching, dandruff, boils, spots etc.

Even if the body cannot use the skin successfully to eliminate excess toxicity, it does not give up trying. The next safest place for it to use is the internal mucosa, that is any moist orifices which are open to the outside world. Eliminating through the mucosa causes illnesses such as coughs, colds, catarrh, diarrhoea, colitis, thrush, cystitis, conjunctivitis, ulcers and heavy clotted periods.

Individuals who still have excess toxicity even though they may be using some of the above methods to eliminate will suffer from symptoms which are caused by toxicity being deposited in the body, usually in the areas of least resistance. Tiredness, irritability, anxiety, depression, arthritis, high blood pressure, heart problems, cancer etc, are all related to the deposition of toxicity.

Needless to say everyone can benefit from a period of detoxification, whether they have serious health problems, just feel below par, or are healthy and want to make sure they stay that way.

HOW COOKING WITHOUT BENEFITS THE BODY

Following the eating regime outlined in this book will automatically reduce the toxic load and improve the level of nutrients available to the body. Also because the diet is easy for the body to assimilate, the food travels quickly through the digestive tract. This not only assists toxicity to be removed from the body, but because the body's work load is reduced, extra energy is released for healing and elimination. The diet is also designed to support the body's blood sugar and by doing so not only does the individual feel better but every organ and system in the body feels healthier and works more efficiently.

HOW BLOOD SUGAR WORKS

We need sugar in order to fuel our bodies and our brains but sugar in the form we tend to think of it (biscuits and sweets or a spoonful in our tea) is not a good fuel. This sugar has been over processed and is too readily absorbed by the body. This causes a sudden surge of sugar to enter into the blood stream and because too much sugar in the blood stream is dangerous, the pancreas is forced to produce insulin to remove this excess. In order to do this the pancreas needs fuel and energy, and so eating sugar robs our body of vital nutrients and overworks the pancreas.

If however we eat sugar in the form of complex carbohydrate foods (rice, millet, root vegetables etc) then the body slowly breaks these down into simple sugars (glucose) and they are steadily released into the bloodstream giving us sustained energy. If we eat more at a particular meal than the body needs then the excess glucose is converted into glycogen and stored by the liver so that mid morning or mid afternoon we can have a top up of blood sugar.

Unfortunately not everyone's liver is giving them a good blood sugar releasing service. This is usually because the liver is struggling to cope with excess toxicity and a lack of nutrients. As far as the body is concerned removal of excess toxicity is more important than giving the body or brain energy and there is a tendency for the liver to say, "Sit down if you are tired or cannot think straight - I've got too much to do". Hence many individuals develop cravings for sugary snacks, tea, coffee or cigarettes in order to boost their blood sugar and the vicious circle starts again.

The only other way to produce energy is by living on the adrenalin which automatically causes blood sugar to be released. Adrenalin however is there for emergency situations, that flight or fight response and is not meant to be lived on daily. Nowadays many individuals have adrenal glands which are becoming exhausted because of this overuse. At one end of the scale are individuals who feel tired and always seem to be pushing themselves to keep going and at the other end we have illnesses such as M.E. In between are a list of symptoms related to low blood sugar (hypoglycaemia) and these can affect not only the physical body but the mental and emotional states as well. They include fatigue, headaches, palpitations, weak or dizzy spells, cold sweats, cravings, fears, lack of concentration or a muzzy head, depression, anxiety and a lack of or excessive hunger. Low blood sugar also has an undermining effect on every other health problem.

By putting Cooking Without into practice, foods eaten at regular intervals are used to keep the blood sugar stable and therefore allow the liver and adrenal glands to recover and the body to obtain sufficient energy to remove excess toxicity.When the blood sugar is more stable you will be aware that your mood and your energy are more even and that you do not develop cravings. Other symptoms related to low blood sugar will also disappear.

When trying to improve health it is important to be aware that our bodies can only produce a certain amount of energy each day and that this energy is needed to detoxify and heal. For instance if you feel a little better and decide to catch up on all those jobs you have left undone, then you may start to feel poorly again because the energy has started going into the jobs rather than into healing. It is therefore important to allow a period of convalescence, when you try to conserve as much energy as possible for the body to use. The body's energy can also be exhausted through stress and worry. Both these can cause the blood sugar to drop even though food may have been eaten at regular intervals. In order to help your body to heal, practice the art of relaxation and avoid stressful situations whenever possible.

One last point about blood sugar. Many individuals feel that their bodies need something sweet, they say that they have a sweet tooth or feel that a meal is not a meal without a pudding. As far as I am concerned there are two main reasons why we crave sweet things. One is because the blood sugar is low (this should not be the case once Cooking Without is put into practice) and the second is because sweet foods are often used as a love substitute. This means that we work hard and push our bodies or give ourselves a hard time mentally by thinking about what we should be doing, rather than treating ourselves with respect and kindness. Suddenly having whipped ourselves we crave something sweet in order to give back to ourselves. The fact that this sweet food often makes us feel worse, either because our blood sugar dips or because we feel guilty causes a vicious circle to be set up. If having put this diet into practice you still crave sweet foods then it may be caused by an emotional problem which needs looking at (see "Emotions, addictions and ill health").

PUTTING COOKING WITHOUT INTO PRACTICE

For at least the first three months of eating this regime I suggest that individuals eat six meals per day! This enables the body to obtain energy from the food rather than using adrenalin or needing the liver to produce blood sugar. The energy which comes from eating regularly will not only enable the individual to feel better but will also enable the internal organs and systems of the body to recover and remove the backlog of toxicity.

Initially food may have to be forced into the body at regular intervals as individuals with low blood sugar do not always feel like eating and can even feel sick at the thought of food. However once the blood sugar is raised by the intake of food, the body seems grateful and will actually start asking to be fed at regular intervals. During this phase you always need to make sure that you have a snack with you wherever you are going in order to keep topping up the blood sugar. Miss the snack and let the blood sugar fall and you will spend the rest of the day feeling under par, chasing your blood sugar but never actually catching it up.

Eventually when the body has removed the excess toxicity and obtained sufficient vitamins and minerals from the improved diet then three meals per day should be adequate, with an occasional piece of fruit in between. By then the liver should be supporting the blood sugar between meals and the adrenalin can be kept for emergency situations. Your body will tell you when you are ready for this; it may be in three months time, it may be in two years time depending on the state of your health when you start detoxifying. Suddenly you will find that you do not feel hungry all the time and your body will happily last from one meal to the next.

WEIGHT CONTROL

Do not worry about putting on excess weight by eating more food more often. You will be amazed at the amount of food you can eat on this regime and the opposite will happen. Provided you are only eating the foods suggested in this book then everything in the body will function more efficiently including the metabolism and the result will be a loss of weight. The art of weight control is to keep the blood sugar stable.

ORGANISING YOUR COOKING

Do not think that Cooking Without is about denying yourself food but rather that it is about building health; eating the right kind of food in sufficient quantities and at regular intervals.

Health is like a bank balance; when we have become ill we have gone into the red. However even though we are in the red we still have to spend energy just to do the bare essentials each day. In order to obtain health we need to minimise the amount of energy spent whilst at the same time putting as much back into the bank as we are able by feeding ourselves as well as possible. In this way we eventually return our health balance to the black and have a few reserves in store for a rainy day.

It only takes a change in attitude to put food and feeding ourselves correctly at the top of our priority list for the day, rather than at the bottom, where it fits in if there is any time left. We would not dream of jumping into the car and covering the warning light up because it was saying that the petrol tank was empty, but how often do we do this with our bodies. By feeding ourselves well today and every day we will have many more years when we can work, look after our families, help others, play sport and live our lives well. If we do not put the effort in now, then we will run out of reserves sooner or later and we will then need others to help us because we will be ill.

Try to organise your cooking so that you have lots of tempting dishes available when you open the fridge door. In this way you will not think about what you cannot eat but rather about what you can enjoy. Put aside a few hours once or twice each week when you switch on the oven and the hotplates and you make quite a few dishes at the same time. If you are chopping vegetables for a casserole, you may as well chop some for a soup and a terrine at the same time. You may as well bake fruit and nut slices at the same time as cooking a nut roast and cornmeal bread.

When cooked, decant some of the food into the freezer for emergency situations or for use later in the week. I like to place a few individual portions in au gratin dishes in the freezer, but you could just fill tupperware dishes with larger amounts. The rest of the food can be kept in the fridge so that for the next few days you have plenty to tempt you when you open the fridge door. If you always keep some brown rice cooked (it will keep up to three days in the fridge) you only need to rustle up a salad or cook some fresh vegetables to complete a meal.

If you have a family who do not want to change their eating patterns to fit in with you, then try making lots of dishes as suggested above, plus a few which they like. Spread the dishes out on the table for a help yourself meal but without making a distinction between their food and yours. Eventually they will start to accept the new regime.

MAKE THE CHANGE GRADUALLY

It is a good idea to transfer yourself gradually onto this regime, perhaps over one to four weeks depending on how good your diet is to start with. The body is used to eating a lot of foods which suppress toxicity and push it back into the cells such as meat, wheat, tea and coffee. By removing or reducing such foods, and increasing the amount of vegetables eaten, toxicity starts to flow out of the cells. However if it flows out of the cells faster than the body can eliminate

11

it to the outside world then excess toxicity floats round in the blood stream making one feel worse rather than better. This may cause a headache, anxiety, tiredness, an upset stomach or can aggravate symptoms already present. If you feel any adverse reactions to the diet then make the changeover to this dietary regime more gradual, but do not give up. Your body is probably saying,"Thank Goodness, at last I can get rid of this toxic, acid waste".

We are so used to not listening to our bodies and panicking when symptoms appear that it takes time to gain an understanding of how the body works and what it is saying. As you gain health, you will also gain confidence in your body and will no longer fear growing old or becoming ill.

VEGETARIANS

This diet is ideally suited to vegetarians. The meat, fish, eggs etc which are allowed are not compulsory and may be omitted. The only effect this will have is to speed up the elimination process still further. If you have suddenly decided to become vegetarian then I suggest that you change over gradually to avoid excess elimination of toxicity and to allow your body to become accustomed to the change.

VITAMIN AND MINERAL SUPPLIMENTS

Nutritional supplements, especially minerals assist the elimination of toxicity from the body. It is however impossible in a book such as this to sugggest levels which would be suitable for all readers. I would suggest that those who wish to assist the detoxification process consult a qualified nutritional therapist. See addresses at the back of this book.

THE DOS AND DON'TS OF COOKING WITHOUT

It is very difficult to write a book with a dietary regime which suits everyone, hence the flexible margins regarding certain foods. It is probably best to err on the side of caution and remove any suspect food for a period of time or until an improvement in health has been obtained. Removal of a substance means that our body loses its adaptability to that food so that if it is causing a problem this will become more apparent when it is re-introduced. Eventually when the toxicity has been removed from the body, the immune system will be stronger and foods which originally caused problems will be able to be re-introduced.

MEAT
To be eaten no more than twice per week, preferably produced organically. Eat poultry and game in preference to lamb. Lamb in preference to beef and avoid pork. Avoid processed and cured meats (sausage, bacon, ham etc)

FISH
Eat fish up to three times per week preferably a selection of oily as well as white fish. Do not eat fish products (ie fish fingers) or smoked fish although frozen fish is acceptable if a fresh supply is unavailable. Tins of salmon, tuna, sardines etc can be used.

EGGS
Up to five eggs per week are acceptable, preferably free range. Up to seven per week if not eating meat or fish. Those with allergies to eggs could try using an egg replacer in baked dishes (see ingredients section).

DAIRY PRODUCE
Avoid all milk, skimmed or whole. Avoid cream and cheese. Yogurt may be acceptable if health problems are not too severe, preferably made from sheep or goats milk. Limit to 2-3 servings per week.

ALTERNATIVE MILKS

Soya milk may be used in moderation, preferably from organic soya beans but without additives such as fruit sugars. Soya yogurt can be bought or made. Do not overuse as soya milk is quite high in fat. Almond or other nut milks can be substituted if soya is not tolerated (see recipes) and rice milk is now available.

VEGETABLES

Approximately 40% of all food consumed should be in the form of vegetables. Aim to consume each day a large varied salad and a good selection of cooked vegetables as well as having at least two days each week completely vegetarian.

Try to vary the vegetables as much as possible and use preferably when in season. If possible buy organically grown.

Use :- Carrots, parsnips, turnips, swede, beetroot, cabbage, brussel sprouts, broccoli, cauliflower, kale, onions, leeks, celery, french beans, runner beans, peas, sweetcorn, marrow, courgettes, lettuce, chinese leaves, radish, cress, fennel, water cress, endive, cucumber, sprouted seeds etc.

The following vegetables should be eaten sparingly:- Peppers, aubergines, potatoes and tomatoes because they are higher in toxicity than other vegetables. Mushrooms because they encourage candida overgrowth and spinach which is high in oxalic acid.

BEANS AND PULSES

These are allowed and can be included in soups, casseroles and salads.

NUTS

Avoid salted nuts and peanuts. Use in moderation as nuts are high in oil and not easy to digest. Use almonds, cashews, hazelnuts and walnuts mainly. Try nut roasts and nut butters.

SEEDS

Use sesame, sunflower and pumpkin seeds and spreads such as tahini.

RICE

Rice is the ideal food to keep the blood sugar stable whilst at the same time soaking up the toxic waste from the body. Preferably use short grain organically grown brown rice. Use without limit but aim to consume between 4 -10 oz of rice weighed before cooking per day.

BUCKWHEAT, MILLET AND QUINOA.

These grains can be used instead of or as well as rice in the form of whole grains or flakes.

CORN

Corn can be used as a thickening agent in the form of flour, for baking in the form of maize meal or as sweetcorn or popcorn. Some individuals do have allergies to corn.

WHEAT

Contains gluten so avoid all wheat products, ie bread, cakes, biscuits, pasta, cereals and flours for at least three months. When wheat is re-introduced, eat it no more than once per day but preferably only 3-4 times per week (see section on why to avoid wheat).

RYE

Contains gluten and should be avoided like wheat. When included it should be used as an alternative to wheat.

BARLEY

Contains gluten and should be avoided initially. It is likely to cause less problems than wheat because it is only used in small quantities in soups and casseroles etc.

OATS

Also contain gluten but are generally more easily tolerated than wheat. Avoid if your health is seriously below par, otherwise include no more than once per day, but preferably only 3-4 times per week.

FRUIT

Limit to one or two fruits per day. Avoid fruit juice or substitute two pieces of fruit for one small glass of fruit juice. Limit tropical fruits and very acidic fruits (oranges, grapefruit, plums, strawberries etc) Apples and pears are the best fruits to be eaten regularly. Fruit may need to be avoided in the early stages of treating candida.

DRIED FRUIT
Use in moderation, preferably unsulphered. Avoid in the early stages of treating Candida or if you suffer from flatulence or bloating.

SUGAR
Avoid all sugar, brown or white. Avoid honey, molasses, malt extract and chemical sugar replacers.

FATS AND OILS
Avoid or limit hardened fats and avoid hydrogenated margarine. Use low salt butter or a non hydrogenated margarine (which is low in trans fatty acids), sparingly for spreading. Use olive oil in any heated dishes and sweat instead of frying whenever possible. Preferably use olive oil for salad dressings (see section on fats).

SALT
Avoid salt completely for three months to allow your natural tastebuds to develop. Use potassium salt substitutes if desired and look out for hidden forms of salt and sodium (see section on why to avoid salt).

YEAST
Avoid yeast, yeast extracts (ie. marmite), shoyu sauce, miso, tamari, vinegar, monosodium glutamate, citric acid, alcohol and stock cubes. Mushrooms, tofu and dried fruit may need avoiding if candida is a problem (see section on candida)

BEVERAGES
Avoid tea, coffee, carbonated soft drinks, squashes and alcohol. For fruit juice - see FRUIT. Substitute with herb teas, barleycup, caro, rooibosch tea, dandelion coffee and filtered water. Beware of additives to all alternatives drinks such as lactose, flavourings etc.

TINNED AND FROZEN PRODUCE
Avoid the general use of tinned produce but the occasional use of tinned tuna, tomatoes, beans etc is acceptable. Limit frozen foods. Frozen fish and meat are allowed but use fresh vegetables for most meals. A few frozen vegetables such as sweetcorn or peas used occasionally are acceptable as they help to make meals more interesting.

WIDENING THE RANGE OF FOODS CONSUMED ONCE HEALTH HAS BEEN OBTAINED

The length of time for which this dietary regime needs to be adhered to will depend on the severity of your health problems. It could be anything from a few months to a few years. Once your health has improved try widening the range of foods consumed but be prepared to go back to the strict regime if you don't feel as well. When re-introducing foods try one new food at a time to see how it affects you.

You should eventually be able to re-introduce wheat, rye, barley and oats but never include wheat more than once per day. A little milk in your barleycup or rooibosch tea is acceptable and cottage cheese and yogurt can be eaten occasionally. Salt is only needed in the occasional soup or casserole. Miso, shoyu and tamari sauce are ideal for flavouring soups and casseroles as they have many beneficial properties. A little cider vinegar, honey, molasses and no sugar fruit spreads can be used in moderation.

Hopefully the benefits you have received from cooking without will encourage you to make this way of eating the foundation on which to build your own, individual diet for life

SUGGESTED MENUS

BREAKFAST SUGGESTIONS

Rice porridge with cinnamon. cloves and dates. Millet porridge with fresh fruit, nuts and seeds. Soaked muesli with fresh fruit and soya milk. Egg fried rice. Scrambled eggs with cornmeal bread.

MID-MORNING

Eat a snack of rice served with fresh fruit and nuts, homemade soup or chopped vegetables etc. If this is not possible eat a second course for breakfast and eat a piece of fresh fruit or some dried fruit and nuts mid morning. Try fruit and nut or savoury rice slices, they are easy to pick up and eat and are delicious.

LUNCH IDEAS

Try homemade soup. Follow with a large mixed salad or rice salad or try stir fried vegetables and rice or a vegetarian savoury with salad.

MID-AFTERNOON

Eat another snack, the size will depend on how late you eat your evening meal. Eat a substantial rice snack if eating your evening meal late or some fruit and nuts, rice slices, rice cakes with nut butter etc if eating earlier.

EVENING MEAL SUGGESTIONS

A fish, chicken or vegetarian savoury served with a good selection of fresh vegetables and / or salad, plus a portion of rice, millet, buckwheat or quinoa

SUPPER

Try soup with rice, porridge, rice with fruit, rice slices, pear and carob delight, apple, date and nut muffins etc.

Eat supper if you feel hungry. Eat supper if you do not normally feel hungry or feel tired at breakfast time as this will help to keep your blood sugar up overnight and enable you to eat a good breakfast. If you normally feel full of energy when you wake it is because your adrenal glands have had a rest, don't live on them, feed them!

INGREDIENTS AND METHODS OF COOKING

BROWN RICE
Some recipes call for cooked rice, some have quantities listed for uncooked rice. If you wish to substitute one for another then rice approximately doubles in weight when cooked. Therefore if a recipe calls for 8oz of uncooked rice and you already have some cooked then substitute 16oz. Rice will keep up to three days if stored in the fridge or it can be frozen for those emergency situations. A tupperware rice container is useful for both sieving and storing cooked rice. Most people find their own favourite way of cooking rice, here is mine.

COOKING BROWN RICE
Soak 8oz short grain brown rice in a pan with lots of cold water for approx 10 mins. This loosens any dirt on the rice and prevents a scum forming when it is cooking. Sieve the rice and place in a pan with 2pts of boiling water. Bring to the boil and simmer for approx 35 mins. There will still be lots of water left in the pan. Pour the rice and water into a sieve and allow to drain. Serve hot or leave to cool in the sieve over the pan with the pan lid on top to prevent the rice drying out. Long grain brown rice does not take as long to cook as short grain rice but cooking times can vary with different batches of rice.

ADDITIONS TO ADD FLAVOUR TO BROWN RICE
Brown rice can be cooked in stock, it can be flavoured with herbs or spices whilst cooking (ie coriander, fennel, bayleaf) or it can be cooked with the addition of such as onion, garlic and fresh ginger. Add more than one flavouring and produce interesting variations. Cooked rice can be flavoured by adding one or more of the following:- toasted sunflower or sesame seeds, slivered almonds, grated orange or lemon rind, fresh herbs (coriander, mint, parsley), olive oil etc.

MILLET, BUCKWHEAT AND QUINOA
These can be used in recipes either instead of rice or served as you would boiled rice. To cook, follow the instructions for cooking brown rice but cook buckwheat and quinoa for approx 10 minutes and millet for approx 18 minutes. Try using in nut roasts, salads, rice slices etc. Millet like rice doubles in weight when cooked. Buckwheat and quinoa treble in weight so if substituting for rice in recipes adjust accordingly.

COOKING BEANS

The length of time cooking takes will depend on the age of the beans (old beans take longer), the size of the beans and the length of the soaking time. Smaller beans and pulses such as lentils, mung beans, aduki beans and split peas can be cooked without soaking. Larger beans need soaking overnight in plenty of boiling water. Discard the soaking water and rinse well before cooking. Even after soaking large beans can take anything up to two hours to cook. This is where I find a pressure cooker invaluable as most large beans can be cooked in only five minutes after an overnight soak. They are not mushy at this stage but are ready to place in such as casseroles and soups. Beans approximately double in size when soaked and cooked

Beans can be frozen at the soaked stage or at the just cooked stage so that a supply is always at hand. Try freezing them in a colander or sieve as this allows any excess water to drain away. The beans can then be tipped into a plastic bag where with a little encouragement they will shatter and become free flowing allowing you to take out just the amount you need at any time.

I always keep a few tins of beans in the cupboard for those emergency situations. They do however contain salt so I discard the liquid and rinse well. Tinned beans do seem to be easier to digest and appear to cause less flatulence.

STOCK

Stock can be made from leftover bones, fresh bones, vegetables and vegetable cooking water.

Vegetables should always be cooked in as little water as possible to prevent the leaching of minerals. However, saving any leftover cooking liquid for soup stock will add flavour and minerals to the soup. I keep a container in the ice box and each day add any leftover cooking water to it. When I am ready to make soup the stock is ready. Do not use stock from cauliflower and other strong vegetables as these will alter the flavour of the soup.

Bones can be obtained from most butchers but do not use bacon bones as these contain sodium. Raw bones produce a better flavoured stock if they are roasted first in a hot oven until brown. Stock made from bones should be brought to the boil and simmered for an hour, making sure that the water level just covers the bones. A pressure cooker saves time when making stock. When cooked, sieve the stock, allow to cool and remove any fat from the surface. Try to cook stock in large quantities and freeze some so that stock is always available.

Fish stock can be made by asking the fishmonger for bones and boiling these in sufficient water to cover them for just ten minutes. Cooking longer gives the stock a strong bitter flavour.

SPROUTED SEEDS
Sprouts can be grown from most whole beans and pulses but your supply needs to be fresh as old seeds do not sprout well. Some of the easiest to grow are lentils, alfalfa, mung and aduki. You can buy special trays in which to grow your seeds but a jam jar will suffice.

Place 1tblsp of the seeds in the jar and soak overnight in lots of cold water. The following morning either fasten a piece of muslin over the jam jar or use the lid to sieve the water from the seeds. Rinse the seeds in more fresh water then drain again and this time leave to stand in a warm preferably dark place (a dark jar can be used). Each morning and evening rinse and drain the jar. In 2-3 days (depending on the warmth) you will have sprouts ready to eat. They are ready when leaves begin to appear.

ORANGE AND LEMON - JUICE AND RIND
Neither of these juices should be used in large quantities as they cause excess elimination from the cells. However they are ideal used in small quantities to add flavour to recipes. I keep ice cubes made from orange and lemon juice in the freezer for such occasions. Orange and lemon rind can also be frozen but preferably buy organically grown fruit as most fruits will have been heavily sprayed. Grate and loosely pack into small containers. If you cannot tolerate citrus fruits leave these flavourings out of recipes.

GINGER
Fresh ginger goes mouldy quite quickly even if kept in the fridge, so peel a large piece of ginger and freeze.Whenever you need ginger for a recipe then grate a little whilst it is still frozen and return the rest to the freezer.

HERBS

I like to use fresh herbs whenever possible so I grow or buy these, chop them and place in small containers in the freezer so that they are always available. If you do not have fresh or frozen herbs, substitute dried herbs but only use one quarter of the fresh amount.

MISO

Although miso is a fermented soya product containing salt, it is such a good food nutritionally that I feel it is worth including in the diet as soon as it can be tolerated. The salt content is approx 8-10%. Some miso does contain barley or rice so check the ingredients. Use miso in the same way as you would use stock cubes by dissolving in a small amount of boiling water.

TAMARI OR SHOYU SAUCE

These are both fermented from soya beans developing a deep rich flavour that tastes saltier than it is. When buying read labels carefully as most supermarket versions contain wheat and monosodium glutamate. As soon as you feel you can tolerate it, use to add flavour to your cooking.

SEAWEEDS

Although seaweeds do contain salt, wash well and use whenever possible in soups, casseroles and salads as seaweed is a very good natural source of vitamins and minerals.

MUSTARD

This is not an easy product to find without added vinegar or wheat but it is available as mustard flour with no other added ingredients and as an English mustard with only salt added (see addresses).

VINEGAR SUBSTITUTES.

Use the equivalent amount of lemon juice or try powdered vitamin C (1/4 tsp for each tablespoon of vinegar).

OLIVES

All olives seem to be preserved in brine but some contain other additives such as citric acid which does need avoiding. Because olives are only used in small quantities, and give a wonderful flavour to dishes I accept the small amount of additional salt. I just wash them well.

TOMATOES
If you cannot tolerate tomatoes but can use miso or tamari, then use these in recipes instead of tomato puree. Where a tin or carton of tomatoes is noted substitute carrot or other vegetable juices.

SUNDRIED TOMATOES
These are available bottled in olive oil although many seem to contain vinegar or citric acid (check labels). I have however found dried ones with no additives. These need soaking in water to soften.

PASTA
This is available made from ingredients such as rice, cornmeal and buckwheat instead of wheat. Spelt from which lasagne and pasta are being made is derived from an ancient wheat grain and although it is not gluten free it seems to cause less problems than modern wheats.

EGG REPLACERS
These are readily available in health food shops. Alternatively an egg replacer can be made by simmering together for five minutes 1 tblsp of flax seeds (can be bought as linusit gold) and 4 fl oz of water. This will produce a mixture which is the consistency of raw egg white and equates with one egg. You do not need to strain the mixture as the flax seeds will just add fibre to your recipe. Egg replacers can be used to bind ingredients together but will not help a mixture to rise.

PUFFED RICE CAKES
These are often used as a substitute for bread and there is no problem with this except that rice cakes contain mainly air and very little rice. Do not use unless accompanied by a substantial meal.

THICKENERS
Cornflour has been used as a thickening agent in some recipes. However other flours can be substituted but the amount used may need to be adjusted. To thicken 3/4 pt of liquid use :-
1 level tblsp of potato flour. 2 level tblsps of rice flour or cornflour.
3 level tblsps of gram flour, soya flour or cornmeal.

RAISING AGENTS
Ordinary baking powder is not acceptable because of its sodium base. Potassium baking powder is available in health food shops. Use as you would ordinary baking powder.

EQUIPMENT

Avoid the use of aluminium pans as this can be seen as a toxic metal. Non stick pans have similar problems. Pressure cookers are usually made of aluminium but are available in stainless steel. A food processor is useful as it is a labour saving piece of equipment. It can be used for slicing, chopping or shredding vegetables and it will also liquidize, puree and mix. If a food processor is not available then in many instances a liquidizer or blender can be used.

ABBREVIATIONS

tblsp = tablespoon.	tsp = teaspoon.	dsp = desertspoon.
lb = pound.	oz = ounce.	gm = gram
fl oz = fluid ounces.	pt = pint.	mins = minutes.
hr = hour.	pkt = packet.	

METRIC CONVERSIONS

1 oz = 28 grams	6 oz = 168 grams	12 oz = 336 grams
2 oz = 56 grams	8 oz = 224 grams	1 lb = 448 grams
4 oz = 112 grams		

GENERAL INFORMATION

I have tried to include alternative ingredients in many instances but this is not always possible without making recipes excessively long. However most recipes will adapt to substitutions. Vegetables can be exchanged in recipes and alternative flours can be used in baking. Egg substitutes can be used in most recipes and nut or rice milk can be used instead of soya milk. Ingredients used to add flavour such as tomato puree, orange juice or lemon rind can be omitted.

Sweating is used in quite a few recipes to impart more flavour. This is not the same as frying as the temperatures used are much lower. It involves softening the vegetables in oil until they begin to brown but it does take time. Allow at least 20 mins and saute vegetables whilst you collect other ingredients together to save time.

Folding is used in a few recipes and involves mixing ingredients using a metal spoon and following a figure of eight movement. This prevents the air being beaten out of the ingredients.

I have kept oven temperatures the same in many recipes so that you can batch cook and put several dishes in the oven at the same time.

BREAKFASTS

BREAKFAST

Breakfast is a very important meal, it is as it says "break fast ". If you have difficulty eating breakfast or feel sick at the thought of it, your blood sugar has dropped too low overnight. Start by eating small amounts of breakfast, perhaps fruit or something light to start with and gradually increase this amount until a substantial breakfast is not only acceptable but is actually desired.

Occasionally it is necessary for some individuals to eat in the middle of the night to prevent the blood sugar dropping so far (eventually when toxicity has been removed and sufficient minerals have been obtained the blood sugar will be stable for longer periods). If the blood sugar is not raised first thing in the morning then individuals often spend all day chasing it but never achieving stability or feeling good however much they eat.

If you like to lie in at the weekends, then take your breakfast to bed with you. Set the alarm as normal, eat your breakfast and go back to sleep, making sure that you are up before your mid morning snack. If you normally feel worse after a lie in it is because your blood sugar has dropped too low by the time you rise.

Although I have tried to make the recipes in this section conform to typical breakfast type dishes, it doesn't really matter what you eat as long as it raises your blood sugar. Some breakfast dishes could be used for meals and snacks during the day ie bubble and squeak for lunch or pear and carob delight as a pudding or supper dish. Other breakfast suggestions include breads from the"baking without" section, rice pudding from the"pudding" section, kedgeree from the "fish" section and eggs, boiled, scrambled or poached .

As all the recipes are gluten free they exclude oats, a delicious breakfast cereal. I have noted where oats can be substituted for those who do not have a problem with gluten. Millet flakes do have a distinctive flavour which does take some adjusting to as do buckwheat flakes which can be used instead of or as well as millet flakes. Linseeds (available in health food shops) have many health giving properties (see fats and oils) and are ideal to sprinkle on breakfast cereals. Store them in an airtight container in the fridge and add 1 dsp to breakfast cereals before serving.

MUESLI

Oat flakes can be substituted for the millet flakes if allowed gluten.
Vary the fruit and nuts so that each muesli you make is different ie.
hazelnut and apricot, raisin and almond or mixed fruit and nut.

7 cups millet flakes	1 cup coconut flakes or
1/2 cup sunflower seeds	1/4 cup desiccated coconut
1 cup nuts	1 cup dried fruit

1   Mix all the ingredients together and store in a container.
2   Serve with soya, almond or rice milk and fresh fruit.

LIGHT MUESLI

Oats can be substituted for the millet flakes if gluten is allowed

4 cups puffed rice cereal	3/4 cup mixed dried fruit ie
3/4 cup mixed nuts	chopped dates, apricots, figs,
1/2 cup sunflower seeds	raisins or sultanas
4 cups millet flakes	1/2 cup desiccated coconut

1   Mix all the ingredients together and store in a container
2   Serve with soya, almond or rice milk.

MILLET PORRIDGE

Ingredients per person
1 cup millet flakes	2 3/4 cups of cold water

I use a tea cup but the size does not matter as long as you keep the
proportions the same. Oat porridge can be made in the same
way for those who can tolerate oats.

1   Place the ingredients in a pan and bring to the boil stirring.
2   Simmer gently for approx 10 mins.
3   Serve plain with soya, almond or rice milk or with fresh fruit,
    dried fruit, nuts and seeds piled on top. These could be added to
    the porridge whilst it is cooking to vary the recipe.

SOAKED MUESLI

Oats can be substituted for the millet flakes if gluten is allowed.

12 oz rice flakes *9 oz millet flakes*
4 oz raisins or *2 oz sunflower seeds*
mixed dried fruit *2 oz nuts*

1 Mix all the ingredients together and store in an airtight container.
2 Fill a breakfast bowl with the muesli and soak in sufficient water to just cover the ingredients. Allow to stand for at least 15 mins or if desired soak over night.
3 Serve with soya, almond or rice milk, soya yogurt or just as it is.

This muesli is ideal to take on holiday as it can be easily made up in hotel bedrooms and can also be used for mid meal snacks. My favourite version of this recipe contains 2 oz of crystallised pineapple instead of 2 oz of the raisins and I use whole almonds for the nuts. The pineapple does contain some sugar so this is a treat to look forward to when health has been obtained.

RICE PORRIDGE

Ingredients per person

1 cup brown rice flakes *2 1/2 cups boiling water*
1/4 tsp cinnamon *1/8 tsp ground cloves*
1 piece fresh fruit ie *1 dsp dried fruit ie*
apple, pear, banana. *raisins, dates*

1 Place all the ingredients except the fresh fruit into a pan, bring to the boil and simmer gently for 10 mins stirring occasionally.
2 Cut the fresh fruit into pieces and add 2 mins before the end of cooking or pile on top just before serving.

Rice flakes vary a lot in the amount of water they soak up so adjust the liquid accordingly.

BREAKFAST RICE

1 bowl of cooked rice per person + a selection from the following

nuts and seeds   *finely diced dried fruit*
desiccated coconut   *stewed dried fruit*
spices eg nutmeg   *chopped fresh fruit*
soya milk, fruit juice   *stewed fresh fruit*
or soya yogurt.   *carob powder*

A good idea is to keep nuts, seeds, toasted nuts and seeds, chopped dried fruit etc in clear glass jars on your worksurface or shelf. Then you can quickly add toppings to a bowl of warm or cold rice. Children love the idea of helping themselves to toppings.

Suggested combinations for 1 bowl of rice

1   1/2 chopped banana, a few raisins, few cashew nuts.
2   1 chopped banana, a few cashew nuts or raisins. Heat in the microwave for 40 secs until the banana becomes soft.
3   1/2 stewed apple, pinch cinnamon, toasted sunflower seeds.
4   1/2 pear, chopped dried apricots, toasted slivered almonds
5   liquidize 1/2 peach and 1/2 banana and pour over the rice
6   stewed prunes and soya yogurt
7   stewed dried apricots and chopped almonds

PEAR AND CAROB DELIGHT

Ingredients per person
2 rounded tblsps   *1 small pear.*
rice flour   *6 fl oz boiling water*
1 heaped tsp carob flour   *1 dsp desiccated coconut*
6 fl oz soya or almond milk

1   In a pan mix the rice and carob flour to a smooth paste with a little soya or almond milk. Gradually add the remaining milk.
2   Cut the pear into thin slices and add to the pan with the coconut
3   Add the boiling water and bring the mixture to the boil stirring.
4   Lower the heat and simmer for 5-10 mins or until the pear begins to disintegrate, sweetening the mixture.

BANANA AND MAIZE BREAKFAST CEREAL

Ingredients per person

2 rounded tblsp   1 banana
maize meal   1 dsp raisins
6 fl oz boiling water   2 drops natural vanilla extract
6 fl oz soya or almond milk

1   Mix the maize meal to a smooth paste with the milk in a pan.
2   Add the vanilla extract, the boiling water, the raisins and the
    finely sliced banana.
3   Bring the mixture to the boil stirring constantly.
4   Lower the heat and simmer for 5-10 mins or until the banana
    begins to disintegrate.

If desired a piece of vanilla pod can be used instead of the extract.

SAGO BREAKFAST CEREAL

Ingredients per person

2 rounded tblsp sago   1/2 banana or pear chopped.
6 fl oz boiling water   2 drops natural vanilla extract.
1 dsp finely chopped dates
6 fl oz soya or almond milk

1   Place all the ingredients into a pan, bring to the boil, stirring
    constantly and then lower the heat.
2   Place a lid on the pan and simmer for 15-20 mins.
3   The fruit should fall to become part of the cereal

If desired a piece of vanilla pod can be used instead of the extract
and an extra dsp of dates used instead of the fruit to sweeten the
cereal.

SOYA MILK YOGURT

1 pt organic soya milk
4 milk free acidophilus capsules

1   Bring the milk to the boil and then allow to cool to body
    temperature (a clean finger is sufficient to test). Cover the pan
    to prevent a skin forming.
2   Empty the acidophilus capsules into a small basin and add 1 tsp
    of the warm soya milk mixing until you have a smooth paste.
    Continue adding the soya milk and mixing until the acidophilus
    is well blended then pour into the pan and stir.
3   Pour the mixture into a warmed vacuum flask, put the top on
    and leave to stand for approx 6 hrs or until the mixture just
    starts to leave the sides of the flask when the flask is tipped.
4   Tip the yogurt out into a container and store in the fridge.

The mixture ideally needs to fill a flask in order for the yogurt to
stay warm. Adjust the quantities if your flask is larger.

Yogurt culture can be bought to use as a starter or use 1tsp of a
bought soya yogurt. Even though these normally contain some sugar
there will be very little in 1 tsp of yogurt. The yogurt will not take as
long to set if using soya yogurt or a culture.

ALMOND MILK

1/2 cup blanched almonds   *2 1/4 cups water.*

1   To blanch the almonds, pour boiling water over the nuts, leave
    to stand for 5 mins. The skins should then easily slip off by
    pressing with the thumb.
2   Place the nuts in the blender and blend until finely ground.
3   Add 1/2 cup of water and blend until a smooth cream is formed.
4   Add the remaining water and blend well.
5   Sieve using a fine sieve. If there is a great deal of pulp left, you
    have not blended for long enough.

Other nuts can be used ie. cashews. The milk will keep for 48 hrs in
the fridge but will separate a little on standing. Shake before using.

BREAKFAST IN A GLASS

1 banana or other soft fruit   *pinch nutmeg*
2 heaped tblsp cooked rice   *3 fl oz soya, almond or rice milk*

1   Place all the ingredients in the processor and liquidize until smooth.
2   Pour into a glass and eat as you would a yogurt

Try substituting other fresh fruits ie. peaches, apricots, mango
or 1tsp carob powder along with the banana

MARMALADE

1/2 lb dried apricots   *2 oranges (preferably organic)*
1/4 pt water   *OR 1 orange and 1 lemon.*

1   Wash the oranges well and squeeze the juice from them .
2   Place the juice in a pan along with the apricots cut into pieces.
3   Bring the apricots and juice to the boil, lower the heat, place a lid on the pan and simmer for approx 10 mins or until the apricots are soft. Add a little water if the mixture starts to become too dry. The amount of water needed and the length of cooking time will be determined by how old the apricots are.
4   Cut the peel from the oranges into matchstick size pieces and place in a pan along with the 1/4 pt water.
5   Bring to the boil and simmer for 10 mins or until the peel is soft.
6   Process the apricots and juice to form a soft smooth puree
7   Mix together the apricot puree, the orange peel and any juices from the pan. Add a little more liquid if the mixture is too stiff.
8   Allow to cool. Place the marmalade into two jars or containers. I suggest you store one in the fridge where it will keep for up to two weeks and the other in the freezer.

APRICOT SPREAD

An apricot spread could be made from the above ingredients but with the orange rind omitted.

EGG FRIED RICE (4)

1 lb cooked rice   *4 dsps water*
4 eggs   *1 dsp olive oil*
black pepper

1 Beat the eggs with the water.
2 Pour 1tsp of oil into a frying pan, heat and add the eggs. Cook as an omelette by lifting the edges of the mixture as it cooks and allowing any uncooked mixture to run to the base.
3 Cut the omelette into little pieces either in the pan or by removing and cutting on a chopping board.
4 Place the cooked egg and rice into the pan along with 1tsp oil and the black pepper. Stir fry until heated through.
5 Add 4 dsps of water and allow this to be absorbed, then serve.

The mixture can be heated through with the water to avoid frying. One tblsp of shoyu sauce will add extra flavour for those allowed this. Try serving egg fried rice with a salad for lunch.

SCRAMBLED TOFU WITH SWEETCORN AND ARAME (4)

8 oz tofu, plain or smoked.   *1tsp olive oil*
4 tblsps arame seaweed   *8 oz sweetcorn kernels*

1 Soak the arame in boiling water for approx 10 mins or until soft. Sieve to remove the water.
2 Place the olive oil in a pan then add the arame, the sweetcorn, and the tofu crumbled into tiny pieces
3 Warm through by stir frying and serve.

Use a dsp of water in the pan if you prefer not to fry. One dsp of shoyu sauce can be added for those allowed this.

RICE WITH LEEKS AND SCRAMBLED EGGS (4)

1 lb leeks, chopped   *1 lb cooked rice*
6 eggs   *black pepper*

1   Cook the leeks in a little water until just tender . Drain well.
2   Warm the rice if not freshly cooked.
3   Beat the eggs with 3 tblsps of water and scramble.
4   Mix all the ingredients together and season with black pepper.

POTATO CAKES (4)

1 1/2 lb potatoes   *3 tblsp rice flour*
1 tblsp olive oil   *black pepper*
Extra flour for shaping

1   Peel, chop and cook the potatoes in boiling water until soft.
2   Sieve and keep the liquid. Mash the potatoes until smooth using
     a little of the cooking liquid to moisten.
3   Add the rice flour and pepper and mix well.
4   Take handfuls of the mixture and roll into balls using rice flour
     to keep the mixture from sticking to your hands. Flatten the
     balls into cakes approx 1/2 " thick.
5   Fry the cakes in a little oil until beginning to brown (approx 5
     mins).Turn and fry the other side.

If allowed serve spread with butter or to accompany other breakfast
dishes. Try substituting parsnips for the potatoes if these cause a
problem.

TRADITIONAL ENGLISH BREAKFAST (4)

4 whole kidneys   *12 oz mushrooms*
4 beef tomatoes   *4-8 potato cakes*
4 eggs   *olive oil and black pepper*

1   Cut the kidneys in half, skin them and remove the core. Brush with oil and sprinkle with black pepper. Grill for approx 5 mins on each side under a medium heat until they are cooked.
2   Cut the tomatoes in half, sprinkle with black pepper and place under the grill with the kidneys 2 mins before the end of cooking. Warm the potato cakes in a similar way.
3   Wash and chop the mushrooms and fry in a little oil until just cooked.
4   Scramble or poach the eggs according to your preference.
5   Assemble the ingredients on to 4 warm plates.

Try to buy organic kidneys and soak overnight in a little soya milk if you prefer a less strong flavour. Organic liver could be used instead. Baked beans bought from a health food shop may be acceptable but check the ingredients first.

SWEETCORN AND ONION FRITTERS (4)

Batter ingredients   *1 lge onion, finely chopped*
2 1/2 oz rice flour   *4 oz sweetcorn kernels*
10 fl oz water   *1 tblsp fresh parsley*
1 lge beaten egg   *olive oil*
black pepper

1   Cook the onion in 2 tblsp water until soft. Drain.
2   Place the sweetcorn kernels in a bowl and roughly mash with the back of a fork until the kernels are just broken.
3   Add the batter ingredients to the bowl along with the onion, parsley and black pepper. Mix well.
4   Fry as two large pancakes in the olive oil until the pancakes are set and golden brown, turning half way through cooking (see the Bubble and Squeak recipe for how to turn).

Try substituting other vegetables and beans in this recipe.

BUBBLE AND SQUEAK (4)

Ideally make this dish with leftover potatoes and cabbage for a quick
breakfast dish. Other leftover vegetables could be substituted for the
cabbage (ie carrots, peas and beans) and parsnips could be
substituted for the potatoes if these cause problems.

1 1/2 lb potatoes   *8 oz white cabbage*
1 tblsp olive oil   *black pepper*

1   Cook the potatoes in boiling water until soft.
2   Chop and cook the cabbage, preferably steamed over the
    potatoes. Do not over cook.
3   Mash the potatoes with a little of the cooking water until soft
    and smooth. Add the cabbage and pepper and mix well.
4   Grease a frying pan with half of the olive oil and fry the potato
    mixture flattened into a pancake shape for approx 10 mins or
    until crisp and brown.
5   Slide the mixture out of the pan onto a chopping board, cooked
    side downwards. Grease the pan with the remaining oil and
    invert the pan over the potato mixture. Lift both the pan and
    the chopping board and turn over so that the mixture tips into
    the frying pan with the uncooked side downwards.
6   Cook for a further 10 mins or until the second side is brown.

POTATO PANCAKES (2-4)

1 egg, beaten   *9 oz grated raw potato*
2 oz rice flour   *1 small onion, grated*
5 fl oz water   *1 dsp chopped fresh parsley*
1 tblsp olive oil   *or other fresh herbs*

1   Mix all the ingredients together, excluding the oil.
2   Fry as one large pancake in half of the oil for approx 15 mins,
    turning the heat low after the first few minutes to prevent
    burning. Turn the pancake and fry in the remaining oil for a
    further 15 minutes. The outside of the pancake should be crisp
    and golden and the potatoes cooked through on the inside.

STARTERS

STARTERS

Starters can be used as snacks, light lunches, or suppers. If you normally have a two course evening meal involving a pudding, then try serving a starter so that you still have a two course meal but you avoid the pudding trap. Puddings can then be saved for weekends.

Many of the salads from the salad section can be served as starters. Try minted avocado and chick peas or curried egg and rice served on a bed of lettuce. If you don't like main course salads then serve a salad starter and benefit from eating more raw vegetables.

STUFFED LETTUCE LEAVES (4)

stuffing
2 oz prawns
2 hard boiled eggs
2 tblsp mayonnaise
2 tblsp grated tofu
1/2 oz ground almonds
1 tblsp fresh herbs ie
parsley, mint, chives
1/4 tsp grated lemon rind

8 lge soft lettuce leaves
french dressing
(see sauces)
cress to garnish

1   Finely chop the eggs and the herbs and then mix all the stuffing
    ingredients together.
2   Divide the stuffing mixture between the eight lettuce leaves, roll
    up and place two leaves on each plate.
3   Garnish with the cress and serve with french dressing.

Those allowed could use cottage cheese instead of the tofu and serve with crusty bread to mop up the juices. Prawns do contain salt unless freshly boiled. Avocado can be substituted for the eggs.

VARIATIONS

Lettuce leaves can be stuffed with a selection of finely chopped or grated vegetables mixed with sufficient mayonnaise or yogurt to bind ie. avocado, tomato, pepper, spring onions, carrot, cucumber, sweetcorn, sprouted seeds. Some brown rice could be included.

SPINACH AND CARROT TIMBALE (4-6)

1 lb spinach	*1 egg*
1 lb carrots	*1/4 tsp nutmeg*
1 clove garlic	*garnish:- sliced tomato and*
black pepper	*toasted sesame seeds*

1   Cook the spinach (in the water which remains on the leaves after washing) for no more than five mins. Drain.
2   Cut the carrots into even sized pieces and cook until just tender.
3   Process the spinach with the egg, the garlic and lots of black pepper until a smooth puree is formed.
4   Puree the carrots with a little of the cooking liquid, the nutmeg and some black pepper.
5   Place a layer of carrot puree, then a layer of spinach puree into 4 au gratin or 6 ramekin dishes.
6   Cook in the oven covered with foil for 10-15 mins or until the spinach puree is set, at Reg 6, 200C, 400F.
7   Garnish with sliced tomatoes and toasted sesame seeds.

WARM CHICKEN LIVER SALAD (4)

8 oz chicken livers	*2 cloves garlic*
3/4 tsp mustard	*1 dsp olive oil*
4 oz continental salad leaves ie	
frisee, radicchio, lambs lettuce	

1   Wash the leaves and arrange on four serving plates.
2   Crush the garlic cloves and cut the chicken livers into small pieces.
3   Heat the oil in a frying pan, add the garlic and cook for a few seconds before adding the chicken livers. Fry quickly until the livers are beginning to brown and are just cooked.
4   Add the mustard and mix in.
5   Spoon the hot livers onto the salad, including any juices from the pan. Serve immediately.

Use coarse grain mustard and organic chicken livers if possible. If allowed add a knob of butter to the oil and mop up the juices with some crusty bread.

AVOCADO DIP (4)

2 ripe avocados
1 clove garlic. optional
pinch chilli powder
black pepper

1 dsp lemon juice
1 tblsp olive oil
1/2 tsp paprika

1   Press the garlic clove and place in a bowl with the rest of the ingredients.
2   Mash with a fork to give a rough textured dip.

A tblsp of mayonnaise can be added if desired.

AVOCADO AND CASHEW NUT PATE (4)

1 med ripe avocado
2 oz cashew nuts
2 hard boiled eggs
4 black olives, optional

1 tblsp lemon juice
1-2 spring onions
1 tblsp fresh parsley
black pepper

1   Mash the avocado and lemon juice with a fork.
2   Toast the cashew nuts, finely grind and allow to cool.
3   Finely chop the spring onion, the parsley, the olives and the hard boiled eggs by hand.
4   Mix all the ingredients together. Add a little water or soya milk if a softer pate is required or if you wish to turn the pate into a dip.
5   Serve with rice cakes, bread, vegetable crudities, salad etc

Butter beans could be used instead of the eggs and other nuts instead of the cashew nuts.

CARROT AND APRICOT PATE (4-6)

3 oz dried apricots
3 fluid oz water
3 oz grated tofu
1/3 tsp cardamom
black pepper

1/4 tsp nutmeg
1 oz ground almonds
8 oz grated carrot
1 tblsp lemon juice

1   Cut the dried apricots into small pieces. Place in the 3 fl oz water and simmer for 10 mins or until the apricots are soft.
2   Mix all the ingredients together by hand including any liquid remaining with the apricots.
3   Place in a small greased loaf tin, cover and bake for 45 mins at reg 6, 200c, 400f.

Cool a little, cut into slices and serve with a salad and rice cakes.

CARROT AND CASHEW NUT PATE (4-6)

9 oz carrots
4 oz cashew nuts
1 tsp chopped mint
1 tblsp orange juice
or soya milk (approx).

1/2 tsp grated orange rind
1 tblsp chopped chives or
spring onions
black pepper

1   Slice and then cook the carrots in a little water until just soft. Sieve and cool.
2   Place the cashew nuts in the food processor and process until finely ground.
3   Add the carrots, mint, orange rind, onions or chives and pepper and process again. If necessary add a little orange juice or milk to obtain a smooth pate.

Serve on rice cakes with a salad garnish or as a sandwich spread. For a variation if allowed add 2 tblsps cottage cheese and mix well.

BUTTERBEAN, TUNA AND MINT PATE.

8 oz of cooked butterbeans,
1 tin tuna in water
1 tsp fresh chopped mint

1 tblsp olive oil
1 tblsp lemon juice
black pepper

1   Drain the tuna fish and place in the food processor with the remaining ingredients.
2   Process until smooth adding a little of the tuna water if necessary to make a soft pate. If you do not have a processor mash the ingredients together in a bowl with a fork.

41

HUMOUS AND CRUDITIES (4-6) ✳

8 oz cooked chick peas	1 clove garlic, optional
3 tblsp tahini paste	2 spring onions
2 tblsp lemon juice	1 tblsp olive oil
little water	black pepper

I cheat if I am in a hurry and use tinned chick peas.

Process all the ingredients until a soft smooth pate is obtained, using a little extra water if necessary.

Humous can be used as a pate, a sandwich spread, a filling for baked potatoes or as a dip with a selection of vegetables crudities to dip in. Crudities could include:- sticks of carrot, celery, pepper and courgette; broccoli and cauliflower florets and whole cherry tomatoes.

AVOCADO AND TOMATO STARTER (4)

1 lge avocado	4 tblsp sprouted seeds ie
1 large beef tomato	lentil, mung, aduki.
1/2 lettuce	4 tblsp french dressing
	(see sauces)

1   Peel, half and stone the avocado. Half the tomato.
2   Lay both the tomato and the avocado halves cut side down and cut each half into 6 wedges.
3   On serving plates arrange beds of shredded lettuce then on top arrange alternate slices of avocado and tomato to form an upturned boat shape
4   Sprinkle with sprouted seeds, and serve with french dressing.

AVOCADO AND MANGO STARTER (4)

Substitute mango for the tomato in the above recipe. Arrange the avocado and mango in a fan shape. For special occasions use the egg and prawn stuffing mixture from the stuffed lettuce leaves recipe and pile at the point of each fan. Pour over the french dressing and for those who can eat bread, use it to mop up the juices. Delicious!

COUNTRY SALAD (4-6)

1 lb waxy new potatoes
3 eggs, hard boiled
bunch asparagus or
green beans
1 lge avocado
French dressing
black pepper

1/2 red pepper, sliced
1/2 yellow pepper, sliced
1 courgette, thinly sliced
12 black olives, optional
1 tblsp fresh parsley
4 spring onions, finely sliced

1   Cook the potatoes whole and in their skins until tender. Cool.
    Peel off the skins if preferred. Cut into large chunks.
2   Shell and quarter the hard boiled eggs.
3   Steam the asparagus or beans for no longer than 5 mins. Cool
    and slice into 1" lengths.
4   Peel and stone the avocado and cut the flesh into chunks.
5   Gently layer the ingredients in a serving bowl so that they look
    mixed but have not been broken by the tossing.
6   Pour the french dressing over just before serving or serve
    separately.

This salad is delicious just as it is but it can have cubes of creamy
goats cheese added and be served with crusty bread for those allowed
such luxuries.

SAVOURY FRUIT SALAD (4-6)

1/2 melon, cubed
1 avocado
1 tblsp lemon juice
2 tblsp olive oil

1/2 cucumber, peeled and diced
2 tomatoes, skinned and diced
1 dsp chopped mint
black pepper

1   Skin and stone the avocado and cut the flesh into cubes.
2   Mix the lemon juice, olive oil and black pepper together.
3   Place all the ingredients in a bowl and mix together very gently.
4   If possible chill for a few hours to allow the flavours to mingle.

Other vegetables and fruit could be substituted in this recipe.

ASPARAGUS OR LEEKS WITH WALNUT MAYONNAISE (4)

1 bunch asparagus or   *8 dsp mayonnaise (see sauces)*
4 long thin young leeks
1/2 oz walnuts, finely chopped

1   If using the leeks, cut off and discard any green section. Cut each stem into two equal lengths

2   If using the asparagus, cut off the woody base of each stem.

3   Steam the leeks or asparagus for 5 mins or until just barely cooked. Cool quickly in cold water then drain.

4   Place the mayonnaise in a bowl and mix in most of the walnuts reserving a few for garnishing.

5   Divide the leeks or asparagus between four plates and spoon the mayonnaise over the centre of each portion.

6   Garnish with the chopped walnuts.

This is a delicious and unusual starter. Use a serrated knife for cutting the leeks; although not tough, they can be difficult to cut. The mayonnaise can be made by substituting 2 tblsp walnut oil for the other oils in the recipe.

HORS D'OEUVRES WITH GARLIC MAYONNAISE (4-6)

mayonnaise   *hard boiled eggs*
(see sauces)   *cherry tomatoes*
2 oz ground almonds   *whole radish*
2 cloves garlic   *black olives*
                                    baby sweetcorn
                                    sugar snap peas

1   Make the mayonnaise using half olive oil and half a lighter oil such as sunflower.

2   Press the garlic cloves and add to the mayonnaise along with the ground almonds. Mix well.

3   Serve to accompany a selection of hors d'oeuvres.

Other vegetables could be used ie cold cooked green beans, broccoli or grilled red or green peppers. Tuna fish or sardines could replace the eggs.

SOUPS

SOUPS

The availability of a good stock makes soup making very easy especially if you are on a yeast and salt free diet. See how to make stock in the ingredients section. I always try to keep a good supply of stock in the freezer but if you do not have stock ready made do not be put off as many of these recipes are fine made with water. Those able to tolerate miso, shoyu or tamari sauce can use these to add extra flavour. However avoid stock cubes in any form. I feel that the hydrolysed vegetable or meat protein which they contain is quite harmful.

A pan of soup is a useful standby. Served with a little rice it makes an ideal mid morning, afternoon or evening snack and it can be used as a starter for lunch or evening meals.

Do not overcook soups. Beans and pulses obviously need cooking well but vegetables can be added at a later point and retain a better flavour and more vitamins if not overcooked. I rarely cook soups (except the beans) in a pressure cooker as overcooking is too easy.

Try cutting the vegetables into different shapes to produce different looking soups ie. carrots can be finely diced, cut into matchstick pieces, sliced, grated, finely chopped in a food processor or left in rough chunks. Each will give the soup a different appearance. Children will often eat soup better when it has been liquidized.

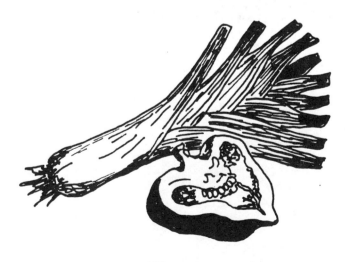

PEA SOUP (4)

6 oz dried whole peas
2 pts water or stock
1 lge onion
2 tblsp fresh parsley
or 1 tsp of dried

1-2 sticks celery
1/2 tsp dried sage
1/4 tsp dried thyme
black pepper

1   Soak the peas overnight in plenty of water.
2   Drain and rinse the peas. Cover with the stock or water, bring to
    the boil and simmer gently, covered with a lid until soft and
    mushy. This will take approx 1-1 1/2 hours but only 10 mins if
    using a pressure cooker. If not using a pressure cooker, you may
    need to add a little more water if the stock is evaporating.
3   Finely chop the celery and onion and add to the soup along with
    the dried sage, thyme, pepper and parsley. If using fresh parsley
    add just before serving.
4   Bring to the boil and cook the soup for a further 15 mins. Blend
    if a smoother soup is desired.

Split peas could be used if a quicker version of the above soup is
required but I feel the whole peas give a nicer flavour. Soak the split
peas for 2 hrs and cook for approx 45 mins

LIGHT LENTIL SOUP (4)

4 oz red split lentils
1 lge onion
1 tsp ground cumin
1/4 tsp ground cloves
1 bayleaf

1 clove garlic
1 tsp grated lemon rind
1 tin chopped tomatoes
1 1/2 pts stock or water
black pepper

1   Wash the lentils, finely chop the onion and press the garlic.
2   Place all the ingredients into a saucepan, bring to the boil and
    simmer for 45 mins.
3   Remove the bay leaf and serve.

This is the soup I make when I am in a hurry. It is so quick and
easy to make and tastes fine even if you don't have any stock.

FENNEL, CELERY AND LEEK SOUP (4)

2 med leeks
1 lge bulb fennel
3-4 sticks celery
1 dsp olive oil
black pepper

3/4 pt stock
1 pt water
1/2pt soya or almond milk
1 tsp celery seeds
1 tsp fennel seeds

1   Finely slice the leeks and celery and dice the fennel.
2   Heat the oil in a pan and add the vegetables plus the fennel and celery seeds. Sweat, stirring occasionally until the vegetables are softened and beginning to brown.
3   Add 1 pt of water, bring to the boil and simmer for 10 mins.
4   Allow to cool a little then process until smooth. This stage can be omitted if you prefer a chunky soup or you do not have a food processor. Return the mixture to the pan.
5   Add the remaining ingredients and bring to the boil.

Extra celery and leeks can be used if you do not have a fennel or they are not in season. Omit the sweating stage if you prefer not to fry or if time is short.

LEEKIE MILLET BROTH (4)

2 lge leeks
2 lge carrots
1 pt stock
1 pt water
1/4 pt soya or
almond milk

1/2 tsp dried thyme
1/2 tsp dried rosemary
black pepper
1 1/2 oz millet flakes

1   Slice the leeks and roughly chop the carrots.
2   Bring the stock and water to the boil and add the leeks, carrots, herbs and seasoning.
3   Bring to the boil and simmer for 15 mins
4   Mix the millet flakes with the milk and stir into the soup. Bring to the boil stirring until thickened and simmer gently for 5 mins.

CARROT AND CORIANDER SOUP (4)

1 lb carrots
1 lge potato
1 lge onion
1 dsp olive oil

1 1/2 pts stock
3 tblsp fresh or frozen
coriander
black pepper

1 Slice the carrots and dice the potato and onion.
2 Sweat the onion and potato in the oil until they begin to soften and brown.
3 Add the carrots, the stock and the pepper. Bring to the boil and simmer for 10-15 mins.
4 Process the soup, return to the pan, add the coriander, heat through and serve.

If you do not have a processor or prefer your soup chunky, then grate the carrots and potato. Sweating can be omitted if desired.

CARROT AND CARDAMOM SOUP (4)

Substitute 2 oz red split lentils for the potato in the above recipe and add 1/2 tsp ground cardamom instead of or as well as the fresh coriander. Add the lentils along with the carrots and cook for 15 mins.

CARROT AND TOMATO SOUP (4)

2 oz cashew nuts
3 med carrots
1 pt stock
black pepper

1 tin chopped tomatoes in juice
1/2 tsp lemon rind
1/2 tsp mustard
1 tblsp chopped fresh coriander

1 Process the cashew nuts until finely ground. Add the carrots and process again until the carrots are finely chopped.
2 Place all the ingredients into a pan, bring to the boil and simmer for 10 minutes.

If you do not have a processor, finely grate the carrots and use ground almonds instead of the cashew nuts.

BUTTERBEAN AND VEGETABLE SOUP (4)

8 oz butterbeans
1 lge parsnip
2 lge carrots
2 leeks or onions

1/4 tsp dried thyme
black pepper
2 pts stock or water

1   Soak the butterbeans overnight in lots of water.
2   Rinse the beans well and cook in the stock or water until soft. Use a pressure cooker if available and cook the beans for 10 mins. The butterbeans can be processed at this stage if a smoother soup is required.
3   Grate the carrots and parsnips and place in the pan with the beans
4   Finely slice the leeks or onions and add to the pan along with the thyme and black pepper. Simmer for 15 mins and serve.

QUICK VEGETABLE AND LENTIL SOUP (4) ✳

1 lge onion
1 turnip
2 lge carrots
3 sticks celery
1 lge leek
4 oz red split lentils
1 clove garlic
1 tblsp tomato puree
(optional)

1/2 tsp dried sage
1/4 tsp marjoram
1/4 tsp rosemary
1/4 tsp oregano
1/2 tsp paprika
1/8 tsp cayenne pepper
1 bayleaf
2 1/2 pts stock or water

1   Cut all the vegetables into small pieces and press the garlic clove.
2   Place all the ingredients into a large pan, bring to the boil and simmer gently for 1/2 hour. Remove the bayleaf.
3   Process if a smooth soup is required and serve.

PARSNIP AND ONION SOUP (4)

2 med parsnips	1/2 tsp curry powder
1 lge onion	1/2 tsp garam masala
2 pts stock	black pepper
1 dsp olive oil	chopped walnuts to garnish

1   Dice the parsnips and onion and slowly sweat in the olive oil until they begin to brown, adding the spices and pepper for the last 2 mins.
2   Add the stock and cook for 15 mins.
3   Process the soup and serve with the walnuts floating on top.

If you do not wish to sweat, omit this stage. If you do not have a food processor grate the parsnip and chop the onion very finely.
1/4 pt of soya or almond milk can be added for a creamier soup.

FISH SOUP (4)

1 lb cod or haddock	2 cloves garlic
2 pts fish stock	juice 1 orange
(see ingred section)	1 tblsp lemon juice
2 med onions	1 bayleaf
1 stick celery	black pepper
1 carrot	1 tblsp fresh parsley
15 oz can chopped tomatoes	

1   Slice the onion, carrot and celery and press the garlic cloves.
2   Place all the ingredients except the fish and the parsley into a large pan. Bring to the boil and simmer for 10-15 mins.
3   Cut or flake the fish into bite sized pieces and add to the soup. Simmer for a further 5 mins or until the fish is just cooked.
4   Serve sprinkled with parsley.

This is a lovely way to eat fish and is ideal for serving to those a little wary of eating fish or to children.

CAULIFLOWER AND CASHEW NUT SOUP (4)

1 onion	*2 oz cashew nuts*
1 leek	*1/2 tsp curry powder*
1 dsp olive oil	*1/2 tsp mustard*
1 small cauliflower	*1/4 tsp thyme*
1 lge parsnip	*black pepper*
1 pt stock	*1 1/2 pts water*

1   Chop the onion and leeks and sweat in the olive oil until they are soft.
2   Break the cauliflower into tiny florets, grate the parsnip and add to the pan along with the stock. Bring to the boil and then simmer for 10 mins.
3   Process the cashew nuts until they are finely ground, then add half of the cauliflower mixture. Process again until smooth and creamy.
4   Return this mixture to the pan along with the remaining soup ingredients.
5   Bring to the boil and simmer for a further 5 mins.

If you do not have a food processor, use ground almonds in place of the cashew nuts and these will thicken the soup.

GAZPACHO (4)

1 lb tomatoes	*2 dsps lemon juice*
1/4 small onion or	*1 clove garlic (optional)*
4 spring onions	*1 dsp fresh chopped*
1 small green pepper	*parsley*
1/2 lge cucumber	*1 dsp fresh chopped*
black pepper	*mint*
extra parsley to garnish	

1   Skin the tomatoes and pepper by placing them in boiling water in a pan for approx 1 min.
2   Roughly cut the vegetables and then process all the ingredients until a smooth mixture is obtained.
3   Serve chilled garnished with parsley.

LEEK, SWEETCORN AND ALMOND SOUP (4)

1 lge onion
1 dsp olive oil
3 sticks celery
1 1/2 lb leeks
3 oz whole almonds
black pepper

1 pt stock
1 1/2 pts water
6 oz sweetcorn kernels
1/2 tsp mustard (optional)
1 dsp fresh parsley

1   Chop the onions, leeks and celery then sweat in the oil until the vegetables are soft and beginning to brown.
2   Process the almonds until they are finely ground, then add 1/2 of the vegetable mixture and approx 1/2 pt of water. Process again until smooth and creamy.
3   Return this mixture to the pan along with the remaining ingredients.
4   Bring the soup to the boil and simmer for 10 mins before serving.

Use ground almonds to thicken the soup if you do not have a food processor.

MAJORCAN SOUP (4)

This recipe is my version of a soup I had on holiday in Majorca. It looked disappointing when it arrived but it turned out to be really delicious despite its simple ingredients. It is a thick stew type of soup but could be served watered down with more stock if desired.

1/2 lb white cabbage
2 onions
6 oz mangetout or
green beans

1 tblsp olive oil
3/4 pt good quality
stock
black pepper

1   Roughly chop the onions and cabbage and sweat them in the olive oil until they begin to soften and brown.
2   Add the beans or mangetout, the pepper and the stock, bring to the boil and simmer for 10 mins before serving.

CHICKEN AND SEAWEED BROTH (4)

I make this soup whenever I have the remains of a chicken carcass, but it can be made without the chicken by substituting vegetable stock.

1 chicken carcass	2 onions
3 pts water	2 carrots
2 strips wakame	3 sticks celery
seaweed	1 dsp olive oil
1 dsp tomato puree	black pepper
(optional)	

1   Cover the carcass with the water, bring to the boil and simmer for 45 mins.
2   Remove any meat from the carcass and keep it to one side. Discard the carcass.
3   Sieve the stock and preferably leave to stand overnight in the fridge to allow any fat to come to the surface.
4   Remove any fat from the stock by laying kitchen roll on the surface and allowing it to soak up the fat.
5   Chop the onions, carrots and celery and sweat in the oil until they begin to soften and brown.
6   Cut the wakame seaweed into small pieces using kitchen scissors. Soak the seaweed in a little water to soften; if necessary.
7   Combine all the ingredients and simmer for 15 mins.

SALADS

SALADS

When you mention a salad to most people it conjures up ideas of lettuce, tomato and cucumber and pangs of hunger for the rest of the afternoon or evening.

Salads need not be so. There is such a wide variety of vegetables, salad ingredients, fruit and nuts which can be used that they never need to be boring. Neither do they need to be lacking in substance. I never serve the typical lettuce, tomato and cucumber unless it is being simply used as a side salad to go along with a substantial meal. Serve instead a selection of salads as a main course so that people can help themselves and pile their plates high. Any leftovers can be used for lunch the next day. In winter serve a warm soup as a starter and a baked potato or hot rice dish with the salads.

Salads are easy to make because the quantity of ingredients is not that important. If you do not have all the ingredients for the following recipes, do not worry; substitute your favourite ingredients or whatever you have available. You can go on inventing new salads for ever.

Salads make ideal starters. If you want a two course meal or don't feel you eat sufficient raw food then try serving some of the following salads as starters.

The following recipes will all serve at least four adults and in many cases there will be some leftover for lunch the next day.

A VARIETY OF SALADS

A delicious meal can be obtained by making lots of different salads out of whatever ingredients you have available. Do not worry about the quantities and use fresh fruit, dried fruit, nuts and seeds as well as vegetables and herbs. Use dressings of mayonnaise, soya yogurt and french dressing where appropriate and try to group ingredients so that colours flavours and textures complement each other.

Below are a list of suggestions and approx quantities. The ingredients just need mixing. Omit the french dressing if desired.

TUNA AND BEAN SALAD :- 1 tin tuna fish (drained), 4 oz red kidney beans, diced flesh of 1 orange, 2 oz toasted cashew nuts, 1tblsp french dressing (optional).

AVOCADO AND GRAPEFRUIT :- diced flesh of 2 red grapefruit, 1 ripe avocado (diced), 1 tsp grated ginger, 1/2 lb spinach leaves (chopped).

COURGETTE AND CAULIFLOWER:- 2 sliced courgettes, 1/2 small cauliflower broken into small florets, 1 tsp caraway seeds, mayonnaise or french dressing.

BEANSPROUT AND SWEETCORN:- 2 oz beansprouts, 4 oz sweetcorn kernels, 1/2 diced cucumber, 2 tomatoes (skinned and diced).

ROOT VEG AND RAISIN :- 1 grated turnip, celeriac or kohlrabi, 1 lge grated carrot, 2 tblsp raisins, 1tblsp french dressing or orange juice.

APPLE, CELERY AND BEETROOT:- 1 large cooked beetroot cubed, 1 stick celery diced, 1 eating apple sliced (leave the skin on), 1 tblsp chopped walnuts, 1tblsp french dressing.

BEAN AND PEPPER :- 8 oz mixed beans, 2 chopped spring onions, 1/2 red pepper diced, 1tblsp fresh herbs, 1tblsp french dressing.

BEAN AND SWEETCORN :- 8 oz red kidney beans, 6 oz cooked green beans (cut into 1" lengths), 8 oz sweetcorn kernels.

CARROT AND BEETROOT:- 8 oz grated raw carrot, 8 oz grated raw beetroot, 2 sticks celery diced, 1oz sultanas, 1-2 tblsps french dressing.

AVOCADO, SMOKED TOFU AND PINEAPPLE:- diced flesh of 1 lge avocado, 6 oz diced smoked tofu, 1 cup chopped pineapple.

BEETROOT AND PINEAPPLE:- 5 med diced beetroot, 8 pitted prunes chopped, 2 tblsp chopped walnuts, 1 cup chopped pineapple, 2 tsps lemon juice.

RICE WITH SWEETCORN AND BEANS :- 4oz cooked brown rice, 2oz sweetcorn, 2 oz red kidney beans, 1 tblsp fresh herbs (mint, parsley, chives etc), 1tblsp french dressing.

RICE AND CARROT :- 4 oz cooked brown rice, 1 grated carrot, 1 stick celery diced, 3 radish sliced, 2 spring onions sliced, 2 tblsps toasted sunflower seeds, 1 tblsp fresh herbs, 1tblsp french dressing.

HAZELNUT AND RICE :- 6 oz cooked brown rice, 2 tblsp raisins, 1/2 tsp ground cinnamon, 2 tblsp toasted, chopped hazelnuts, 2 tblsp toasted sesame seeds, 6 chopped dried apricots, 1 tsp grated ginger, 1-2 tblsps french dressing.

LEAF GREENS, ARAME AND SATSUMAS :- chopped greens (lettuce, spinach, chinese leaves, watercress), 1 oz arame seaweed soaked in water until soft, 2 satsumas segmented, french dressing.

BROCCOLI AND RED BEAN :- 1 lb broccoli florets, 8 oz red kidney beans, 2 sticks celery sliced, 2 spring onions sliced, french dressing.

PINEAPPLE AND OLIVE :- salad greens (chinese leaves, spinach, cress), 1/2 cup pineapple pieces, 12 black olives, 2 tomatoes cut into segments, 2" piece cucumber cubed.

AVOCADO, SWEETCORN AND OLIVE :- 1 avocado diced, 3 tblsp sweetcorn, 12 black olives halved, 1 tblsp french dressing.

The following salads also make excellent accompaniments to curries.

CUCUMBER, MINT AND YOGURT :- 1/2 cucumber peeled and diced, 1" piece ginger grated, 1 tblsp chopped mint, 5 fl oz yogurt.

TOMATO AND CORIANDER :-5 lge tomatoes skinned and sliced, 1 tblsp chopped fresh coriander, 2 spring onions finely sliced, french dressing.

APPLE, CARROT AND GINGER :- 1 grated apple, 1 lge grated carrot, 1 heaped tsp grated ginger, 1tblsp french dressing.

ALL IN ONE SALAD

One of my favourite meals is a bowl of salad which contains anything I have available. Serve this on its own, with a baked potato or boiled new potatoes or with a savoury rice salad.

In a large bowl put ANY of the following ingredients in ANY quantities until you have sufficient salad. Mix gently and serve, dressed if you like with french dressing.

Shredded lettuce, spinach, chinese leaves, white cabbage or red cabbage. Grated carrot, parsnip, celeriac or kohlrabi. Diced cucumber, avocado, peppers, tomato, fennel, peach or apple. Sliced celery, radish, spring onion or courgettes. Florets of cauliflower and broccoli. Sweetcorn kernels, fresh peas, broad beans, olives or grapes. Cooked beans ie.chick peas or red kidney beans. Chopped, flaked or toasted nuts and seeds. Fresh herbs ie. mint, chives, parsley. Watercress, mustard cress, sprouted seeds.

COLESLAW

1/2 lb white cabbage	Dressing
1/2 bulb fennel or	3 tblsp olive oil
2 sticks celery	1 tblsp lemon juice
1 small eating apple	1/2 tsp mustard
1 tblsp sultanas	1/2 tsp grated ginger
1 lge carrot	1 spring onion
2 tblsp chopped walnuts	

1　Shred the cabbage and fennel finely. Chop the celery and the apple leaving the skin on the apple. Grate the carrot.
2　Shake the dressing ingredients together in a screw topped jar.
3　Mix all the coleslaw ingredients and the dressing together in a bowl.

An alternative coleslaw can be made by adding 4 tblsps mayonnaise instead of the dressing.

CURRIED APPLE COLESLAW

1/2 lb white cabbage	Dressing
2 lge sticks celery	*3 tblsp mayonnaise*
1 red eating apple	*3 tblsp soya yogurt or*
8 radish	*extra mayonnaise*
2 spring onions	*1 dsp lemon juice*
2 tsp caraway seeds	*1/2 tsp curry powder*

1 Shred the cabbage. Slice the radish, the celery, the spring onions and the apple leaving the peel on the apple.
2 Mix the dressing ingredients together.
3 Combine all the ingredients in a large bowl.

If preferred a french dressing could be used instead of the mayonnaise and yogurt.

MINTED AVOCADO AND CHICK PEA SALAD

4 oz chick peas	*1 tblsp lemon juice*
1 lge banana	*1 clove garlic, optional*
1 med ripe avocado	*1 tsp fresh mint*
paprika to garnish	*3 tblsp mayonnaise*

1 Cook the chick peas until tender and allow to cool.
2 Slice the banana and dice the avocado flesh into a bowl. Toss gently in the lemon juice.
3 Stir in the remaining ingredients and garnish with paprika.

This salad makes a lovely starter served on a bed of crisp lettuce.

CHICKEN, EGG, ALMOND AND POTATO SALAD

8 oz new potatoes
2 hard boiled eggs
4 tblsp mayonnaise

4 oz cooked chicken
2 oz toasted flaked
almonds

1   Cook the potatoes in their skins and when cool skin and dice.
2   Roughly chop the chicken and hard boiled eggs
3   Mix all the ingredients together.

Avocado can be used if you cannot tolerate eggs.

TUNA AND CELERY SALAD

1 tin tuna in water
2 sticks celery

4 oz cooked rice
mayonnaise, yogurt
or french dressing

1   Cut and finely dice the celery and combine with the rice and
     drained tuna.
2   Use sufficient french dressing, mayonnaise or yogurt to bind the
     ingredients. I like to use a mixture of yogurt and mayonnaise.

JELLIED BEETROOT SALAD

1/2 pt orange juice
1/2 pkt (5 1/2 gms) gelatine
or gelozone if vegetarian

3/4 lb cooked beetroot

1   Warm the fruit juice in a pan and sprinkle the gelatine on top.
     Stir until dissolved.
2   Cube the beetroot and add to the pan. Mix.
3   Pour into a serving dish and refrigerate until set.

JELLIED CARROT SALAD

Follow the jellied betroot recipe but add 1/2 lb finely grated raw
carrot instead of the beetroot. Try other flavoured fruit juices.

MILLET TABOULI

3 oz whole millet
3 lge tomatoes
1/4 red pepper
1/4 cucumber
1 stick celery

2 tblsp french dressing
1 heaped tblsp fresh
chopped mint (essential)
1 tblsp chopped parsley
1 tsp chopped chives

1   Cook the millet in 3/4 pt of boiling water for 10-15 mins. Sieve
    the millet and allow to cool.
2   Skin and finely chop the tomatoes. Finely dice the pepper,
    cucumber and celery.
3   Mix the millet, salad vegetables, herbs and french dressing
    together and leave to stand for a few hours to allow the flavours
    to mingle.

Tabouli is traditionally made with couscous which is made from
wheat. Use this if you are allowed as it is delicious. Just add the
uncooked couscous to the salad instead of the millet. It will soften by
soaking up the juices. Allow to stand for 2 hrs before serving.

MEDITERRANEAN LENTIL SALAD

6 oz whole lentils
2 tblsp olive oil
1 tblsp lemon juice
1/2 tsp lemon rind
1 clove garlic
1 tsp fresh parsley,
chives and mint

1 orange
1/2 tsp orange rind
2 tblsp currants
2 spring onions
1 small carrot
1/4 red pepper
1/4 green pepper

1   Cook the lentils for approx 15-20 mins in lots of water until soft
    but not mushy. Drain.
2   Chop the orange flesh and press the garlic clove.
3   Add to the lentils along with the oil, lemon juice and the orange
    and lemon rind whilst the lentils are still warm. Allow to cool.
4   Grate the carrot, dice the peppers, slice the spring onions and
    finely chop the herbs.
5   When cool, combine all the salad ingredients and if possible
    stand for 1 hr before serving to allow the flavours to mix.

RICE PILAF RING

1 tblsp olive oil	*1 1/2 oz raisins*
1 lge onion	*1 1/2 oz dried apricots*
8 oz brown rice	*2 oz walnuts*
1 pt water	*1/2 tsp cinnamon*
1 bayleaf	*black pepper*
2 tblsp french dressing	

1   Dice the onion and sweat in the oil for approx 10 mins.
2   Soak the rice in cold water for 15 mins. Rinse and drain.
3   Finely chop the apricots and walnuts and add to the pan with the rice, the raisins, the spices and the black pepper.
4   Bring to the boil, cover and simmer for approx 40 mins until the rice is cooked and all the water has been absorbed. Add a little more water if necessary, during cooking.
5   Remove the bayleaf and stir in the french dressing while still warm. Press into a ring mould and leave to cool.

Serve as it is or fill the centre with tropical curried chicken or minted avocado and chick pea salad. The french dressing can be omitted and the pilaf should stick together provided the rice has been cooked sufficiently.

RED CABBAGE SALAD

1 lb red cabbage	*juice 1 orange*
1 onion	*2 tsps lemon juice*
1 lge baking apple	*1/2 tsp orange rind*
2 tblsp raisins	*1/2 tsp lemon rind*
2 fl oz water	

1   Chop the red cabbage, slice the onion and grate the apple
2   Mix all the ingredients together in a casserole dish. Cover and cook in the oven at reg 6, 200c, 400f for approx 1 hr, stirring once during cooking.

This dish can be served hot as a vegetable or allowed to cool and be served as a salad. It can be cooked on the top of the stove but be careful as it will quickly dry and burn.

CURRIED EGG AND RICE SALAD

Avocado can be substituted for the hard boiled eggs.

6 oz brown rice	*3 tblsp mayonnaise*
1 med onion	*3 tblsp soya yogurt*
1 tsp curry powder	*or extra mayonnaise*
2 tsps tomato puree	*4 hard boiled eggs*
1 tsp paprika	

1   Cook the rice and allow to cool.
2   Finely dice the onion and cook in 2 tblsp water for 5 mins.
3   Stir the curry powder, paprika and tomato puree into the onions and allow to cool.
4   Coarsely chop the hard boiled eggs and then stir all the ingredients gently together.

TROPICAL CURRIED CHICKEN SALAD

Vegetarians could substitute butter beans

12 oz cooked chicken	Dressing
2 bananas	*4 tblsp mayonnaise*
1 tblsp lemon juice	*2 spring onions*
2 oz toasted cashews	*1/2 tsp curry powder*
1 oz sultanas	*1/2 tsp lemon juice*
2 oz dried apricots	*1/4 eating apple*

1   To make the dressing, slice the spring onions and finely grate the apple before combining all the ingredients.
2   Slice the bananas and toss in the lemon juice to prevent browning.
3   Cut the chicken into bite sized pieces and dice the apricots into small pieces.
4   Place all the ingredients together and gently mix.

This makes a delicious filling for the rice pilaff ring or it can be served as one of a selection of salads or as a starter on a bed of lettuce garnished with toasted coconut.

MAINLY VEGETARIAN

VEGETABLE CHILLI WITH WALNUTS AND QUINOA (4) ✳

4 oz quinoa
1 pt carrot or tomato
juice
1 onion
1 carrot
2 sticks celery
1 tblsp olive oil
black pepper

1/2 red pepper
2 courgettes
juice and rind 1 orange
4 oz walnut halves
8 oz cooked red kidney
beans
2 tsps paprika
1/2 tsp nutmeg

1   Cook the quinoa in 3/4 pt boiling water for 15 mins.
2   Dice the onion, carrot and celery and sweat in the oil until they
    begin to soften and brown.
3   Finely dice the courgettes and the red pepper. Add to the pan
    along with the other vegetables and continue to sweat until they
    are beginning to soften.
4   Process 2/3 rds of the walnuts until they are finely ground and
    add these to the vegetables along with the remaining walnuts
    broken into smaller pieces and the quinoa mixture.
5   Add the remaining ingredients, mix well and spoon into a large,
    shallow au gratin dish and bake uncovered in the centre of the
    oven at reg 6, 200c, 400f for 30 mins.

If you do not have a food processor use ground almonds instead of
the ground walnuts. Millet could be used instead of the quinoa and
other favourite vegetables substituted..

If you prefer not to fry miss out the sweating stage.

LENTIL BOLOGNESE (4) ✳

4 oz brown lentils	*1 pt creamed tomatoes*
1 onion	*or tomato juice*
1/2 green pepper	*1 tsp oregano*
1 carrot	*1 tsp basil*
1 stick celery	*1 dsp tomato puree*
2 cloves garlic	*1 bayleaf*
1/2 pt water	*black pepper*

1   Wash the lentils well.
2   Finely chop the onion, green pepper and celery. Dice the carrot and press the garlic cloves.
3   Place all the ingredients into a pan, bring to the boil and simmer covered for 30 mins or until the lentils are soft but not mushy.

Serve with rice or pasta, as a filling for baked potatoes, as a stuffing for vegetables or taco shells or in a lasagne. I always make up double the quantity of this recipe as it freezes well and is a super standby. If tomatoes are not tolerated use carrot juice and miss out the tomato puree.

LENTIL MOUSSAKA (4)

1 portion lentil bolognese

1 1/2 lb potatoes	*3 courgettes*
1 dsp olive oil	*1 aubergine*

1   Place half the lentil mix into a large shallow ovenproof dish
2   Slice the courgettes and aubergine into 1/2" slices and place in layers on top of the lentils. Cover with the remaining lentil mix.
3   Peel the potatoes and cut into 1/8" slices, using a food processor if available. Layer these on top of the lentils and vegetables.
4   Brush the top with olive oil and bake at reg 6, 200c, 400f for 1 1/4 hrs until the potatoes are cooked and crisp.

Serve with salads

VEGETARIAN SHEPHERDS PIE (4) ✳

1 portion lentil bolognese
1 1/2 lb potatoes
1 dsp olive oil

1   Cook the potatoes until soft and mash with a small amount of the cooking liquid until they are soft and fluffy.
2   Place the lentil bolognese into a shallow ovenproof dish
3   Spread the potatoes on top, level the surface and brush with olive oil.
4   Bake for 3/4 hr at reg 6, 200c, 400f. Place under the grill for a few minutes if the surface has not browned sufficiently.

An alternative topping could be made by mixing cooked millet and mashed parsnips in roughly equal quantities.

CARROT AND COURGETTE BAKE (4)

1 onion diced
2 grated courgettes
2 grated carrots
1 dsp olive oil
1/2 tsp rosemary
1/2 tsp thyme
1/2 tsp potassium B.P.

2 eggs
4 fl oz soya or almond milk
2 oz maize meal
1 oz rice flour
black pepper

1   Sweat the onion in the oil until it begins to soften and brown.
2   Mix in a bowl the onion, courgettes and carrots.
3   Beat the eggs with the maize meal, rice flour, milk, BP and herbs. Combine the two mixtures.
4   Pour into a greased au gratin dish and bake uncovered for 3/4 - 1hr or until brown and set. Reg 6, 200c, 400f.

Serve with a selection of salads and baked potatoes.

MILLET AND WALNUT BAKE (4)

1 pt tomato, carrot or veg juice
1 pt water   *2 med courgettes*
4 oz millet grain   *4 oz walnuts*
1 onion   *black pepper*
1 carrot   *1/2 tsp rosemary*
1 lge stick celery   *1/2 tsp thyme*
1 tblsp olive oil

1   Mix the vegetable juice and the water and cook the millet for 20
    mins in 1pt of this mixture.
2   Finely chop the onion and celery, finely dice the carrot and
    courgettes. Grind the walnuts in a food processor until they are
    roughly ground.
3   Sweat the onion, carrot and celery in the oil until they start to
    soften and brown. Add the courgettes and sweat for a few more
    mins.
4   Add the millet mixture, the remaining liquid, the nuts, herbs
    and pepper.
5   Mix well and place in a large, shallow, ovenproof dish.
6   Bake uncovered in the centre of the oven for 30 mins at reg 6,
    200c, 400f.

Serve hot with salads, vegetables or baked potatoes.
Omit the sweating if you prefer. Other vegetables can be substituted
for a variation on the above recipe.

The original recipe for this dish uses couscous or bulghur wheat
instead of the millet. If you are allowed wheat try it as it really does
make a delicious bake. Just add 3 oz of couscous or bulghur along
with the remaining ingredients and add a total of 11/2 pts of liquid
including the veg juice. The couscous or bulghur will soak up the
liquid as it cooks. A little grated cheese on top of this will make even
the most ardent meat eaters start thinking vegetarian.

CAULIFLOWER AND COURGETTE BAKE (4)

1 1/2 lb cauliflower
2 courgettes
1 dsp olive oil
3 eggs, separated

1/4 pt soya or almond milk
1 tsp mustard
3 tblsp rice flour

1   Divide the cauliflower into small florets. Cook for approx 5 mins in boiling water until it is just tender.
2   Slice the courgettes and sweat in the olive oil until they begin to soften and brown.
3   Mix the flour and mustard with the milk in a pan and then gently bring to the boil and simmer for 1 min stirring all the time. The sauce will be very thick.
4   Blend the cauliflower, egg yolks and white sauce in a food processor until smooth.
5   Whisk the egg whites until stiff and fold into the cauliflower mixture with a large metal spoon.
6   Spoon half the mixture into a greased au gratin dish, arrange the courgettes on top saving a few for garnishing, then cover with the remaining cauliflower mixture and the reserved courgettes.
7   Bake at reg 6, 200c, 400f, for approx 30 mins or until golden brown and set.

Serve hot with potatoes or rice and salads or vegetables.

SAVOURY PANCAKES (4)

1 egg   *8 fl oz water or a mixture*
4 oz rice flour   *of water and soya milk*
1 dsp olive oil   *1 level tsp potassium B.P.*

1 Blend all the ingredients except the oil in the food processor. If
  mixing by hand, beat the egg then add the remaining
  ingredients except the oil and beat well.
2 Oil a griddle or pan and cook 4 pancakes. Turn as soon as the
  pancakes are puffed and full of bubbles.

RATATOUILLE STUFFED PANCAKES

Fill four pancakes with ratatouille (see index) and place in one large
or four small au gratin dishes. Cover with white sauce (see index)
and sprinkle the surface with chopped nuts or if allowed a mixture of
breadcrumbs and grated cheese. Place in a hot oven or under the
grill to warm through and brown.

VEGETABLE MASALA PANCAKES

Follow the above recipe but use the vegetable masala ingredients to
stuff the pancakes (see index).

LENTIL BOLOGNESE PANCAKES

Follow the above recipe but use the lentil bolognese ingredients to
stuff the pancakes (see index).

Stuffed pancakes take a little time to prepare but are worth the
effort for special meals. Even confirmed meat eaters will love them.
To save time pancakes can be made in bulk and frozen.

BLACK EYED BEAN AND VEGETABLE TERRINE (4)

6 oz black eye beans
1 lge onion
2 sticks celery
1 courgette
1 med carrot
1 dsp olive oil
1 clove garlic
1/2 tsp grated
lemon rind

1/2 tsp basil
1/4 tsp thyme
1 tsp grated ginger
1 dsp fresh parsley
1 dsp fresh coriander
black pepper
4 oz cooked rice

1　Soak the black eye beans overnight and cook until they are quite soft. Sieve to remove the cooking liquid

2　Finely dice the onion, celery and the courgette, grate the carrot and press the garlic clove. Sweat the onion, celery and garlic in the oil until they begin to soften and brown. Add the courgette and carrot and continue cooking until they too begin to soften.

3　Finely chop the parsley and coriander and place in a bowl along with the rest of the ingredients. Mix the ingredients together but do not be gentle as the beans should partially break up making the mixture quite soft.

4　Place in a greased loaf tin and bake in the centre of the oven at reg 6, 200c, 400f for approx 45 mins until the loaf is beginning to brown around the edges.

Serve hot or cold with a selection of vegetables or salads.
Substitute cooked millet or quinoa for the rice if desired.

NUTTY VEGETABLE LOAF (4)

1 onion
1/2 red pepper
1 dsp olive oil
1 med carrot, grated
1/2 med baking apple,
grated
black pepper
4 oz cooked brown rice
or buckwheat or millet

2 oz nuts, finely ground
1 dsp tomato puree
1/4 tsp thyme
1/4 tsp rosemary
1/4 tsp nutmeg
1/8 tsp cayenne pepper
1 tsp mustard, optional

1   Finely dice the onion and red pepper and sweat in the oil until they soften and begin to brown.
2   Add the grated carrot and apple and sweat for another few mins until they too begin to soften.
3   Combine all the ingredients and mix well.
4   Place the mixture into a greased loaf tin and bake covered for approx 40 mins in the centre of the oven at reg 6, 200c, 400f.

Serve hot with vegetables, salads, rice or potatoes and with a sauce from the sauces section (fresh tomato, onion, vegetable puree etc) Serve cold with a selection of salads. 1tsp miso can be used instead of the tomato puree and the vegetables can also be varied.

SQUIRREL'S DELIGHT (4)

1 onion	*1/2 tsp grated lemon rind*
1 clove garlic	*2 tsp lemon juice*
2 oz mushrooms,	*2 tblsp fresh parsley*
(optional)	*black pepper*
1 stick celery	*1 tblsp fresh coriander*
1 dsp olive oil	*1 level tsp ground coriander*
2 oz chopped almonds	*1/2 level tsp cinnamon*
3 oz chopped cashews	*2 pinches ground cloves*
1 oz ground almonds	*1/4 tsp fennel seeds*
2 eggs	*4 oz cooked millet, rice*
3 tblsp sweetcorn or	*quinoa or buckwheat.*
peas	

1   Finely dice the onion, celery and mushrooms and press the garlic clove.
2   Sweat the onion, garlic and celery in the oil until they soften and begin to brown. Add the mushrooms and saute for 2 mins.
3   Mix all the ingredients together.
4   Place in a greased loaf tin and cover with foil.
5   Bake at reg 6, 200c, 400f for approx 45 mins. For a more moist loaf steam over a pan of water for 45 mins or pressure cook for 15 mins.

Serve hot with vegetables, salads, rice or potatoes and with a sauce from the sauces section (fresh tomato, onion, vegetable puree etc)

NUT ROAST (4)

1 small onion	*1/4 tsp rosemary*
1 dsp olive oil	*1/4 tsp thyme*
2 lge mushrooms or	*2 oz hazelnuts*
1 stick celery	*1 oz cashews*
1 lge tomato	*1 oz almonds*
1 tsp rice flour	*4 oz cooked rice*
3 fl oz water or stock	*1 egg (can be omitted)*
black pepper	

1   Finely dice the onion, mushrooms (or celery), and skin and dice the tomato.
2   Sweat the onion in the oil until soft. Add the mushrooms or celery and cook for 2-3 mins. Stir in the tomato, cover and simmer for 3 mins.
3   Sprinkle on the flour and cook stirring for 1 min. Add the stock or water gradually, stirring as you add. Add the herbs and cook for 2 mins.
4   Grind the nuts roughly and add along with the rice, egg and pepper
5   Pack the mixture into a terrine or loaf tin, cover with foil and tuck the edges under to secure tightly.
6   Steam for 45 mins above a pan of boiling water or alternatively pressure cook for 15 mins.

This loaf remains moist because of the way it is cooked. It can be served hot and is delicious served with the orange and ginger sauce from the vegetable and fruit kebab recipe. However it can also be served cold with salads or as a pate.

The original recipe contained 2 oz breadcrumbs instead of the rice so try this as a variation if you are allowed bread. If permitted use 1/2 tsp miso to make a tasty stock.

VEGETABLE AND FRUIT KEBABS WITH ORANGE AND GINGER SAUCE (4)

Kebabs	Sauce
2 corn on the cob	1/4 pt orange juice
8 med mushrooms	1 tsp grated orange rind
2 lge courgettes	1 tsp grated ginger
1 red pepper	2 dsps sunflower oil
2 bananas	1 tsp mustard
4 lge or 8 sml	pinch cayenne pepper
skewers	black pepper
	2 cloves garlic
	1/2 pt good stock
	1 level tblsp cornflour

1   Make a marinade by mixing all the sauce ingredients except the stock and cornflour.
2   Cut the sweetcorn, courgettes, pepper and bananas into 8 pieces. Place all the vegetables and fruit into a tupperware container with a tight fitting lid. Pour over the marinade and allow to stand for at least 2 hrs, turning the container occasionally to coat the vegetables with the marinade.
3   Thread the kebab ingredients onto 4 lge or 8 sml skewers.
4   Place the kebabs on a baking tray, cover with foil and bake in the oven at reg 6, 200c, 400f for 30 mins
5   Pour the remaining marinade into a pan together with the stock and the cornflour. Mix until smooth and bring the sauce to the boil stirring constantly.When the kebabs have cooked pour any juices from the tray into the sauce.

Place the kebabs on a bed of rice and serve with the sauce poured over. Accompany with a crisp salad.

If fresh sweetcorn is not available use frozen. Use a carton of orange juice rather than fresh oranges as this is not quite as acidic and makes the sauce less sharp. Another vegetable could be substituted for the mushrooms ie.onion or tomatoes and cubes of chicken or lamb could be used instead of the bananas. Two tblsps of shoyu sauce added to the sauce will add extra flavour (if allowed) and will enable water to be used instead of the stock.

VEGETABLE RISOTTO (4) ✳

6 oz brown rice   handful beansprouts
2 carrots   2 tblsp sweetcorn
1 sml parsnip   2 oz toasted slivered almonds
1 stick celery   1 tblsp parsley
1 onion   2 tblsp water
1 courgette   black pepper
1 dsp olive oil

1   Boil the rice until it is just cooked, sieve and keep warm.
2   Peel the carrots and parsnips and then using a vegetable peeler
     continue peeling so that the vegetables form into thin slivers.
3   Dice the onion and celery and slice the courgette.
4   Sweat the vegetables in the olive oil starting with the onion and
     celery and then add the carrot, parsnip and courgette.
4   Add the beansprouts and sweetcorn last of all prior to adding
     the almonds, rice, parsley, pepper and water. Mix well, heat
     through and serve.

Add 1 tsp finely sliced fresh ginger to add extra flavour or if
acceptable 1 tblsp shoyu sauce. Vary the vegetables to add interest to
your risottos (ie green beans, mangetout, broccoli, cauliflower) and
use millet, buckwheat or quinoa instead of the rice.

STIR FRIED VEGETABLES WITH TOASTED CASHEWS (4)

Choose 6 vegetables from the following

1 onion
1 carrot   1/2 pt good stock
2 sticks celery   1 level tblsp cornflour
1/2 pepper   4 oz toasted cashews
2 courgettes   1 tblsp olive oil
4 oz mushrooms
12 baby sweetcorn
16 sugar snap peas or mange tout
4 oz green beans
2 oz water chestnuts

1   Cut the vegetables into shapes which will cook in equal times.
2   Sweat the vegetables in the oil until they begin to soften and brown.
3   Add the stock, cover and cook for a few more minutes.
4   Mix the cornflour to a smooth paste with a little water and add to the vegetables stirring all the time. Bring to the boil and simmer until the mixture thickens.
5   Add the cashews and serve.

Serve with plain boiled rice, millet or quinoa and with a side salad. A variation to the above recipe can be achieved (if allowed), by dissolving 2 tsps light miso, 2 tsps tomato puree and 2 dsps shoyu sauce in 1/2 pt of boiling water. Use this instead of the stock. You will not need to add the cornflour as this produces a delicious thickened sauce.

BRAZILIAN STIR FRY (4)

Select 6 of the following veg
2 onions
2 carrots
2 sticks celery
12 baby sweetcorn
8 oz broccoli florets
2 courgettes
2 oz green beans
2 oz mange tout
4 oz mushrooms
1/2 pepper

2 oz creamed coconut
1/2 pt boiling water
2 oz ground almonds
1/2 tsp grated fresh ginger
black pepper
1/2 tsp thyme
1 tblsp olive oil

1   Dissolve the creamed coconut in the boiling water.
2   Cut the vegetables into pieces which will cook in equal times.
3   Sweat the vegetables in the oil until they are all just cooked.
4   Add the coconut water, the ground almonds, the ginger, the thyme and some black pepper. Heat through and serve

Use bought ground almonds as these need to be very finely ground to thicken the sauce.
For a variation add 5 oz smoked tofu or some cooked chicken instead of one of the vegetables.

BROCCOLI AND SWEEETCORN QUICHE (4)

Cabbage leaves are used instead of pastry in this quiche

6-8 lge cabbage leaves	*3 eggs*
1 lb broccoli florets	*3/4 pt soya or almond milk*
2 lge onions	*1 tblsp fresh parsley*
8 oz sweetcorn kernels	*black pepper*
1 dsp olive oil	*2 oz ground nuts*

1   Cook the cabbage and the broccoli in boiling water for approx 5 mins until the cabbage leaves are soft enough to line the dish and the broccoli is still crunchy.
2   Cool the broccoli quickly by dipping in cold water to prevent overcooking.
3   Chop the onions and sweat in the oil until they begin to brown and soften. Mix in the parsley.
4   Beat the eggs and milk and season with black pepper.
5   Use the cabbage leaves to double line a deep 10" quiche dish.
6   Scatter half the onions over the base, then arrange the broccoli florets around the dish making sure that they do not come above the top of the dish or they will burn.
7   Fill the gaps between the broccoli with sweetcorn, then scatter the remaining onions over the top. The dish should be well packed with vegetables.
8   Pour over the egg and milk mixture and scatter the ground nuts over the surface.
9   Bake at reg 6, 200c, 400f for approx 40-50 mins or until the centre of the quiche is just setting. Do not overcook or the eggs start to curdle and spoil the quiche.

Other ingredients could be used to make quiches, such as tuna fish, prawns, cubed smoked tofu, spinach, mushrooms, courgettes and peppers.

If you cannot eat eggs, try using 15 oz silken tofu and 9 fl oz soya milk instead of the eggs and milk. The flan will set but will not rise as it would when using eggs.

CARROT AND LEEK QUICHE (4)

For the base :- 1 quantity rice pancake mixture (see index)

8 oz mushrooms or	*3 eggs*
smoked tofu	*3/4 pt soya milk*
11/4 lb leeks	*1 tblsp fresh parsley*
1 dsp olive oil	*2 oz ground nuts*
2 med carrots, grated	*black pepper*

1 Make 4 pancakes using the rice pancake mixture and use to line a greased, deep 10" flan dish.
2 If using the mushrooms, slice and sweat in the oil until they begin to soften and brown.
3 Trim the green leaves from the leeks and slice the white sections. Cook the leeks in a little water until they are almost tender. Drain well and mix in the parsley.
4 Beat the eggs with the milk and season with black pepper.
5 Layer half the carrots and leeks in the flan dish and then the mushrooms, or cubed tofu. Repeat with a second layer of carrots and leeks.
6 Pour over the eggs and milk, then sprinkle with the ground nuts.
7 Bake for 40-50 mins at reg 6, 200c, 400f until the centre of the flan is just setting. Do not overcook or the eggs will start to curdle.

If you cannot tolerate mushrooms or tofu substitute another vegetable such as green beans or courgettes. Alternatively tuna fish or red kidney beans could be used. If you cannot eat eggs, try using 15 oz silken tofu and 9 fl oz soya milk instead of the eggs and milk. The quiche will set but will not rise as it would when using eggs.

POTATO, COURGETTE AND AUBERGINE BAKE (4) ✳

2 1/2 lb potatoes
2 onions
1 aubergine
4 courgettes
1 lb spinach
olive oil

1 tin chopped tomatoes
in tomato juice
1 tsp oregano
6 sun dried tomatoes
10 olives, halved

1   Finely slice the potatoes and the onion and then slice the courgettes and the aubergine into 1/2" slices. Lightly cook the spinach in the water which remains on the leaves after washing.
2   Layer half the potatoes in a large greased au gratin dish or roasting tin.
3   Place half the sliced onions on top and then all the aubergines and courgettes.
4   Mix the tinned tomatoes with the oregano and spread on top of the vegetables.
5   Sprinkle the chopped sun dried tomatoes and the olives over the surface.
6   Cover with a layer of spinach, then the remaining onions and the potatoes.
7   Brush the surface with olive oil and bake in the centre of the oven at reg 6, 200c, 400f for 1 1/4 hrs. Cover with foil if the potatoes start to brown too much.

Serve with salads.

Use a food processor to slice the potatoes if possible as this means they will be finely sliced and will cook easily. Tuna fish makes a good substitute for the olives and sun dried tomatoes and mushrooms could be used instead of the spinach. Note, the only acceptable sun dried tomatoes I have found are dried and need soaking to reconstitute.

POLENTA PIZZA (4)

4 oz polenta
or maize meal
1 pt water
1 tblsp olive oil
2 tblsp tomato puree
1/2 tsp oregano
olive oil for dribbling
on the surface

Toppings to choose from:-
sliced peppers
finely sliced onion
sliced spring onions
sliced tomatoes
sweetcorn kernels
artichoke hearts
sliced mushrooms
sliced courgettes
black or green olives
sundried tomatoes
pine nuts
pineapple
tuna fish
prawns
sardines
garlic

1   Mix the polenta or maize meal with 1/4 pt cold water in a pan
     (preferably a non stick one) Add 3/4 pt of boiling water, mixing
     as you add.
2   Bring to the boil and simmer over a low heat, stirring constantly
     for 5 mins. The mixture should be thick and smooth. Beat in the
     olive oil.
3   Grease a 10-12" pizza pan or similar sized baking tray and
     spread the hot mixture over the surface forming a pizza base.
4   Spread the tomato puree on top and sprinkle with oregano.
5   Add the toppings of your choice making sure you build up a
     substantial layer.
6   Drizzle the surface with olive oil and bake in a preheated oven
     at reg 6, 200c, 400f for 30-35 mins.

The base will remain soft and will need careful handling when
serving. Serve along with a selection of salads.
Add a few slivers of goats cheese to the topping if allowed.

VEGETABLE LASAGNE (4)

Lasagne
4 oz polenta
1 pt water
1 tblsp olive oil

White sauce
3/4 pt soya or
almond milk
2 level tblsp cornflour
1 tsp mustard
1/4 tsp nutmeg
black pepper

Filling
3 onions
2 courgettes
2 sticks celery
1 carrot
1/2 tsp basil
1/2 tsp oregano
2 dsps tomato puree
2 fl oz water
10 black olives
6 sundried tomatoes
1 dsp olive oil

1 Mix the polenta with 1/4 pt of cold water in a pan. Add 3/4 pt of boiling water mixing as you add. Bring to the boil and cook for 5 mins stirring constantly. Add the olive oil and mix well.

2 Grease a baking tray which is twice the size of the dish you intend to use for the lasagne. Spread the polenta onto the baking tray making a thin sheet. Allow to cool and cut in half then use the sheets of polenta instead of lasagne.

3 To make the filling:- Dice the onions, courgettes, celery and carrot and chop the sun dried tomatoes. Sweat the vegetables in the olive oil until they begin to soften. Add the remaining filling ingredients and mix well.

4 To make the white sauce:-In a saucepan, mix the cornflour with the mustard and a little milk until smooth. Add the remaining sauce ingredients and bring to the boil stirring constantly.

5 To assemble the lasagne:- Place half the vegetable mixture into an au gratin or lasagne dish and cover with a sheet of polenta. Repeat with the remaining vegetables and polenta. Pour the white sauce over the surface.

6 Bake for approx 40 mins at reg 6, 200c, 400f .

SEAFOOD LASAGNE :- Use tuna fish and prawns instead of the olives and sun dried tomatoes in the above recipe.

LENTIL LASAGNE :- Use the lentil bolognese recipe instead of the vegetable mixture in the above recipe.

STUFFED BAKED POTATOES (4)

4 lge baking potatoes
filling (see below)

1   Wash the potatoes and prick the skins to prevent bursting.
2   Bake for 1 1/4 hrs in the centre of the oven at reg 6, 200c, 400f .
3   When cooked split the potatoes in half and roughly mash by
    pressing a fork into the flesh. Pile one of the following fillings
    into the centre.

MUSHROOM AND TOMATO
Saute 6 oz sliced mushrooms in a little oil, add the diced flesh of 4
skinned tomatoes and 12 quartered olives. Heat through but do not
cook or the tomatoes will become too soft.

TUNA, CELERY AND EGG OR AVOCADO
Mix a tin of drained tuna fish with 2 diced hard boiled eggs (or 1
avocado), 2 large sticks celery diced and 4 tblsp mayonnaise.

TAHINI AND TOMATO
Scoop the flesh out of the potatoes and mash in a bowl with 4 tblsp
of tahini, the flesh of 4 tomatoes skinned and diced and 1 dsp of
tomato puree. Pile back into the shells and sprinkle the surface with
sunflower seeds.

CHICKEN OR BUTTERBEAN WITH SWEETCORN
Make a white sauce (see sauces section) and add 6oz cooked chicken
(or cooked butter beans), 4 tblsp sweetcorn and 1 tblsp of fresh
chopped herbs ie. parsley, tarragon or coriander.

PRAWNS WITH SWEETCORN AND CELERY
Mix 4 oz prawns with 4 tblsp of sweetcorn kernels, 2 large sticks of
celery diced and 4 tblsp of mayonnaise.

Other fillings which could be used include, humous, ratatouille, lentil
bolognese, avocado and cashew nut pate, coleslaw, tropical curried
chicken salad or minted avocado and chick pea salad.

WINTER BEAN AND TOFU CASSEROLE (4)

1 whole corn on the cob	8 oz cooked red kidney beans
1/2 small swede	1/2 tsp thyme
1 lge parsnip	1/2 tsp rosemary
2 med onions	1 bayleaf
2 carrots	black pepper
2 courgettes	10 fl oz water
6 oz plain tofu	10 fl oz soya or almond milk
	2 level tblsp cornflour

1   Cut the corn on the cob into 1/2" sections.
2   Cut the vegetables into chunks adjusting the size according to how quickly they will cook. Place all the vegetables into a casserole dish.
3   Cube the tofu and add to the casserole along with the kidney beans, herbs, pepper and the water. Mix gently.
4   Cover the casserole and cook for 1 hr at reg 6, 200c, 400f.
5   When cooked, lift out the vegetables and tofu using a slotted spoon and remove the bayleaf.
6   Mix the soya or almond milk to a smooth paste with the cornflour and add to the juices in the casserole dish. Bring to the boil on top of the cooker stirring constantly and simmer for 2 mins. Return the vegetables to the pan and gently mix.

This is a delicious casserole for a cold winters day. Serve it along with rice, millet, quinoa or baked potatoes and a salad, or crusty garlic bread if allowed.

A tblsp of shoyu sauce can be added for extra flavour if tolerated. Other beans and other vegetables can be substituted to vary this casserole.

BEAN AND VEGETABLE CASSEROLE (4)

2 oz red split lentils	1 onion
1 lge tin chopped	1 lge carrot
tomatoes in juice	1 parsnip
1 clove garlic	2 sticks celery
1 tsp paprika	2 courgettes
1 tsp grated ginger	4 oz green beans
1 tsp ground cumin	8 broccoli florets
1 tsp ground coriander	1/2 pt water
black pepper	
1 bayleaf	
6 oz cooked beans (chick peas, black eye, kidney, etc)	

1   Place the lentils, the tomatoes, the pressed garlic clove, the ginger and the spices into a casserole dish and mix.
2   Chop the vegetables into chunks, varying the size according to how quickly they will cook. Place on top of the lentil mix along with the cooked beans.
3   Pour the water over the ingredients but do not mix at this stage. The lentils need to stay at the bottom of the casserole in the liquid in order to cook.
4   Cover the casserole and bake in the centre of the oven at reg 6, 200c, 400f for 1 hr mixing gently half way through.

Remove the bayleaf and serve with rice, millet, quinoa or baked potatoes and a salad. Those allowed could use crusty bread to mop up the juices.

A variety of casseroles can be made by substituting other ingredients. Use carrot juice or other vegetable juice instead of the tomatoes. Use other herbs instead of the cumin and coriander ie. 1 tsp dill seeds, 1 tsp fennel and 1/2 tsp marjoram. Substitute other vegetables ie. peppers, leeks, fennel, cauliflower, kohlrabi, turnip, celeriac. Buckwheat could be used instead of the beans to produce a buckwheat and vegetable casserole. Cook the buckwheat first for 12 mins in lots of water then drain and add to the casserole.

Extra flavour can be added for those allowed by including 1 tsp miso dissolved in a little boiling water or 1 tblsp of shoyu sauce.

BROCCOLI AND SMOKED TOFU BAKE (4)

8 oz broccoli florets
1 med onion
2 level tblsp rice flour
1/2 pt soya milk
1/4 tsp nutmeg
1/2 tsp lemon rind
black pepper
8 oz smoked tofu
8 oz cooked red kidney beans

Topping
3 oz millet flakes
1 oz brown rice flour
2 oz ground nuts ie.
almonds, hazelnuts
2 dsps sunflower oil
2 tblsp sunflower seeds

1   Chop the onion and cook with the broccoli in 1/4 pt of boiling water until just tender. Drain and keep the cooking liquid.

2   Put the rice flour in a pan and mix to a smooth paste using a little soya milk. Add the remaining soya milk and the stock from the vegetables made up to 1/4 pt with water.

3   Bring to the boil, stirring constantly, then lower the heat and simmer for 2 mins.

4   Add the nutmeg, lemon rind and pepper, then the vegetables, beans and the tofu which should be cubed.

5   Spoon the mixture into a large au gratin dish (or 4 small dishes).

6   To make the topping, place the millet flakes, rice flour and ground nuts into a bowl and rub in the oil by hand.

7   Spread the topping over the vegetable and tofu mixture and scatter the sunflower seeds over the surface.

8   Bake for 15 mins or until the topping is brown at reg 6, 200c, 400f on the top shelf of the oven.

VEGETABLE CRUMBLE (4)

Follow the above recipe but substitute a 1 lb selection of vegetables instead of the tofu and kidney beans (try leek, parsnip, carrot, celery, courgette, sweetcorn) Cook all the vegetables together in just over 1/4 pt of water and add 1/2 tsp rosemary and 1/2 tsp thyme to the sauce. Keep the remaining ingredients the same and cook for 15 mins as above.

VEGETABLE AND CASHEW NUT MEDLEY (4)

6 oz broccoli
1 courgette
1-2 sticks celery
1 leek
1 med carrot
3 oz green beans
1/2 red pepper
1 tsp olive oil
4 oz whole cashews

Sauce
1 tsp tomato puree
1 tsp grated ginger
2 tsps lemon juice
1/2 tsp grated lemon rind
2 tblsp orange juice
1/4 tsp nutmeg
1 tsp paprika
1 tblsp fresh coriander
1 rounded dsp cornflour
12 fl oz stock (use veg water)

1   Break the broccoli into small florets and cut the beans in half. Slice the courgette, celery, red pepper and leek and cut the carrot into matchstick pieces. Toast the cashews.
2   Place the vegetables into a pan with 1/2 pt boiling water. Bring to the boil and simmer for 5 mins or until the veg are just cooked but slightly crisp. Drain, keeping the liquid for stock.
3   To make the sauce, place all the sauce ingredients except the stock into a pan and mix to a smooth paste. Add the stock gradually.
4   Bring to the boil stirring and allow to simmer for 2 mins.
5   Add the vegetables and cashew nuts to the sauce and allow to heat through.

Serve in individual au gratin dishes or as a sauce to go with rice or pasta. Accompany with salads.

Other vegetables which substitute well in this dish include onions, baby sweetcorn, water chestnuts, mangetout or sugar snap peas. Try walnuts or toasted slivered almonds instead of the cashews. If it is tolerated add 1 tblsp of shoyu sauce to the sauce ingredients.

POTATO AND PARSNIP PIE CRUST

Potatoes and parsnips are used to make a pie crust which can then be filled with one of the following fillings or one of your choice.

1 lb potatoes
3/4 lb parsnips
black pepper
olive oil for brushing

1   Cut the potatoes and parsnips into equal sized chunks and cook together in boiling water until tender.
2   Sieve and save the cooking liquid.
3   Mash the potatoes and the parsnips with some black pepper and sufficient cooking liquid to make them soft and smooth.
4   Press into a greased 9" pie dish moulding with the fingers to form a pie shape. Brush the surface with olive oil and bake in the oven for 45 mins at reg 6, 200c, 400f.

SPINACH AND EGG FILLING (4)

4 hard boiled eggs   *1 lb spinach*
paprika   *3/4 pt white sauce (see index)*

1   Halve the hard boiled eggs and lay cut side down into the pie.
2   Shred the spinach and then cook in the water in which it has been washed for no more than 5 mins or until it is soft and wilted. Drain and spread over the eggs.
3   Make the white sauce as directed and pour over the eggs and spinach. Sprinkle with paprika and serve.

RATATOUILLE FILLING (4)

Add 2 oz toasted pine nuts and a few chopped olives and sun dried tomatoes to the basic recipe (see index). Fill the pie and serve.

STIR FRIED VEGETABLE FILLING (4)

Stir fry a 11/2 lb selection of vegetables, pile into the pie and serve Sprinkle with a little grated cheese if allowed.

STUFFED PEPPERS (4)

1 onion	4 med peppers
1 clove garlic	4 tblsp sweetcorn kernels
1 dsp olive oil	1 dsp fresh chopped mint
8 oz cooked rice	1 dsp fresh chopped parsley
2 dsps raisins	1/2 tsp ground cinnamon
2 tblsp pine nuts or	1/2 tsp ground cardamom
cashew nuts	black pepper

1   Chop the onion and sweat along with the pressed clove of garlic until they begin to soften and brown.
2   Add all the remaining ingredients except the peppers and mix well.
3   Cut a circular hole in the top of each pepper removing the stalk. Use a spoon to scoop out any internal fibres or seeds.
4   Hold each of the peppers in turn over the pan containing the stuffing mixture. Using a spoon fill each pepper with the mixture and press it down well.
5   Place the peppers in a deep sided ovenproof dish. Cut a little off the base of the peppers if necessary to enable them to stand easily.
6   Pour 1/4 pt of water around the peppers and cover with foil. Bake in the centre of the oven at reg 6, 200c, 400f for 50-60 mins or until the peppers are soft but not mushy.

Serve as a vegetarian main course with vegetables and salad or as a vegetable accompaniment.
Note that red peppers are sweeter than green peppers.
Peppers could also be stuffed with nut roast or millet and walnut bake ingredients.

STUFFED AUBERGINES (4)

2 lge aubergines	1/2 tsp marjoram
1 onion	1/2 tsp oregano
1 clove garlic	1 dsp fresh chopped parsley
12 black olives	1 dsp fresh chopped coriander
4 med tomatoes	black pepper
1 tsp tomato puree	2 oz cooked rice
olive oil	2 oz ground almonds

1   Cut the aubergines in half and scoop out the flesh leaving 1/2"
    around the edge next to the skin. Dice the flesh finely and place
    in a large bowl.
2   Finely dice the onion and press the garlic clove. Sweat the onion
    and garlic in a little olive oil until they begin to soften and
    brown. Add these to the diced aubergine flesh in the bowl.
3   Skin the tomatoes and dice the flesh. Quarter the black olives.
    Add to the bowl along with the remaining ingredients and mix.
4   Place the aubergine shells on a baking tray, au gratin dish or in
    individual dishes.
5   Pile the stuffing into the shells, pressing down firmly.
6   Dribble the surface with olive oil, cover with foil and bake at reg
    6, 200c, 400f, for 1 hr until the aubergines are quite soft.

Serve with salad and vegetables as a main course or individually as
starters.

Millet or quinoa could be used instead of the rice. The original recipe
used 4 oz breadcrumbs instead of the rice and ground almonds. If
permitted try this for a variation. Half a tin of flaked tuna fish or 2
tblsps grated cheese can be added for extra flavour if allowed. Meat
eaters will begin to think vegetarian after eating this.

STUFFED MARROW

Use the same mixture to stuff rings of marrow. Peel the marrow, cut
into 1 1/2" slices and remove the centres. The centres can be finely
diced and added to the filling ingredients removing any large seeds
which may be present. Bake for approx 1/2 hr.

Two different ways of serving rice to accompany meals

RICE WITH SWEETCORN AND COCONUT (4)

4 oz sweetcorn kernels
or cooked peas
8 oz cooked rice

3 dsp desiccated coconut
1 oz creamed coconut
3 fl oz water

1   Break the sweetcorn kernels (or peas) in a bowl with a fork.
    Dissolve the creamed coconut in the boiling water.
2   Add all the ingredients to the pan and bring slowly to the boil
    stirring frequently.
3   Turn off the heat and leave to stand, covered for 5 mins.

CARROT AND COCONUT RICE (4)

8 oz cooked rice
1 oz creamed coconut
3 fl oz boiling water

8 oz carrots, grated
1/2 tsp ground nutmeg
5 cardamom pods or
1/2 tsp ground cardamom

1   Dissolve the creamed coconut in the boiling water.
    If using cardamom pods, split the pods and remove the seeds
    throwing away the empty shells
2   Place all the ingredients into a pan and bring slowly to the boil
    stirring frequently.
3   Cover and simmer for 4-5 mins, or until the carrots are cooked.

SUSHI

2 sheets sushi nori (toasted dried seaweed)
1 portion of rice with sweetcorn or carrot and coconut rice.

1   Lay the sheets of nori on a flat surface and divide the rice
    between them. Spread the rice out, pressing it down and keeping
    it 1" away from the farthest and nearest edges
2   Roll up the nori sheets like a swiss roll, dampening the farthest
    edge so that it sticks to itself and seals the roll.
3   Allow to cool. Cut the sushi roll into 1" slices to serve as snacks
    or cut into 3" lengths to serve with vegetables or salads.

INDIAN FOOD

Indian food fits very well into this eating regime. It is an ideal way to entertain as a wide selection of dishes can be offered most of which are allowed. Try the following four dishes but also include the chicken curry, the spicy baked chicken or the lamb korma from the meat section. Add a few salads which can be used as curry accompaniments (ie. apple, carrot and ginger, cucumber, mint and yogurt or tomato and coriander) and some naan bread or poppadoms for those allowed wheat. Who would mind being on a special diet

VEGETABLE MASALA (4)

1 1/2 lb selection of veg ie.
cauliflower florets	*1 tsp garam masala*
onion	*1/2 tsp ground cumin*
leek	*1/2 tsp ground coriander*
courgettes	*1/4 tsp ground cardamom*
carrots	*1/2 tsp fennel seeds*
mushrooms	*1/2 tsp tumeric*
broccoli	*1 tsp grated ginger*
green beans	*1 tblsp lemon juice*
celery	*2 oz ground almonds*
sweetcorn	*2 oz creamed coconut*
1 tblsp olive oil	*1/2 pt water*

1   Cut the vegetables into shapes which will cook in roughly equal times. Sweat the vegetables in the olive oil until they begin to soften and brown.
2   Add the spices to the pan and sweat for another 2 mins.
3   Dissolve the coconut milk in the boiling water and add to the vegetables along with the lemon juice, ginger and ground almonds. Stir to mix.
4   Simmer for another few mins until all the vegetables are just cooked. Add a little more water if the mixture starts to become too dry. Serve with rice, millet or quinoa.

BIRIANI WITH RICE (4)

2 onions
2 med baking apples
1 1/2 pts water
1 clove garlic
1 tsp grated ginger
2 oz ground almonds
2 oz split red lentils

1 dsp tomato puree (optional)
2 oz creamed coconut
1 tsp ground fennel
1/2 tsp ground cardamom
1 tsp ground cumin
1 tsp ground coriander
1 tsp garam masala
1 tsp tumeric

1   Finely dice the onions, grate the baking apples and press the garlic clove. Wash the red lentils.
2   Place all the ingredients into a saucepan, bring to the boil and simmer gently for 30-40 mins until the lentils have fallen to form part of the sauce. Stir occasionally whilst cooking.
3   Serve with plain boiled rice

QUICK BEAN CURRY. (4)

2 oz creamed coconut
1/2 pt boiling water
1/2 pepper, diced
1 onion, diced
3 oz sweetcorn or peas
8 oz cooked beans
1 clove garlic, pressed

1 tsp grated ginger
1 tsp ground coriander
1 tsp ground cumin
1 tblsp fresh chopped coriander
1 lge tin chopped tomatoes in tomato juice

1   Dissolve the coconut in the boiling water in a saucepan.
2   Add the remaining ingredients, bring to the boil and simmer for 15 mins.

MUSHROOM CURRY
Add 3/4 lb of small button mushrooms instead of the beans to the above recipe.

VEGETABLE ROGAN JOSH (4)

6 med onions	1 tsp ground coriander
2 cloves garlic	1 tsp ground cumin
1 tblsp olive oil	1 tsp fennel seeds
1 tsp grated ginger	1 tsp garam masala
1 pt creamed tomatoes	1 tsp paprika
or tomato juice	1/2 tsp tumeric
1 1/2 lb vegetables ie	1/4 tsp cardamom
carrot, celery, pepper,	ground or seeds
mushrooms, fennel,	

okra, baby sweetcorn, broccoli, courgettes.

I like to select just two or three vegetables and for instance make a mushroom and courgette rogan josh or an okra, baby sweetcorn and fennel rogan josh. The variations are endless.

1   Dice the onions and press the garlic cloves. Sweat the onions and garlic gently in the olive oil until they are a golden brown colour. This will take at least 1/2 hr, don't rush, don't turn the heat up too high and stir frequently
2   Make the creamed tomato juice up to 1 1/2 pts with water.
3   Process half of the onions with half of the tomato juice until they are smooth and creamy.
4   Add the spices to the pan with the remaining onions and continue to sweat for 2-3 mins stirring constantly.
5   Add the onion and tomato mixture, the remaining tomato juice the ginger and the vegetables cut into chunks. Stir to mix.
6   Bring to the boil and simmer for 15-20 mins or until the vegetables are just cooked.

Serve with rice, millet or quinoa and a salad.
If you wish to avoid sweating just process 3 raw diced onion with the tomato juice and add to the pan with the remaining ingredients.The curry will however have less flavour.

VEGETABLE AND FRUIT ROGAN JOSH

Try adding 1/2 diced mango, 1 sliced banana or 2 tblsp chopped pineapple just before the vegetables have finished cooking.

MEAT DISHES

CHICKEN POLO (4)

2 onions	1 tblsp raisins
1 clove garlic	2 oz dried apricots
1 dsp olive oil	1 cinnamon stick or
8 oz chicken breasts	1/2 tsp cinnamon
1 lge carrot	1 bayleaf
8 oz short grain rice	black pepper
3/4 pt stock or water	2 oz split almonds

1   Chop the onion, press the garlic and cut the carrot into matchstick pieces. Cut the chicken into bite sized pieces and the apricots into small dice.
2   Sweat the onion and the garlic in the oil until they begin to brown. Use a heavy bottomed pan with a good fitting lid.
3   Add the chicken and saute for a few mins until the chicken is starting to brown. Wash the rice well and add along with the remaining ingredients (except the almonds).
4   Bring to the boil and simmer gently for 40-50 mins until the rice is cooked. A little more water or stock may be needed near to the end of the cooking time to prevent the mixture sticking to the pan. The rice should be creamy and sticky when cooked.
5   Toast the almonds and stir in just before serving.

CHICKEN CURRY (4)

8 oz cooked chicken	1 tsp hot madras curry powder
1 lge onion	1 pt water or stock
1 lge baking apple	2 tblsp sultanas
1/4 green pepper	1 tblsp desiccated coconut
1/4 red pepper	1 tblsp tomato puree
1 clove garlic	1 rounded tsp cornflour
1 stick celery	black pepper

1   Dice the onion, celery, peppers and the chicken and grate the baking apple. Press the garlic clove.
2   Place all the ingredients except the cornflour into a saucepan, bring to the boil and simmer for 50 mins stirring occasionally.
3   Mix the cornflour in a little water and stir into the curry to thicken. Re-heat and cook for 2 mins before serving.

CHICKEN BRAZILIAN (4)

3-4 chicken breasts
1 tblsp lemon juice
1 tblsp olive oil
2 cloves garlic
2 onions
1 tblsp parsley

1 green pepper
2 lge tomatoes
2 oz ground almonds
2 oz creamed coconut
1/4 pt boiling water
black pepper

1   Cube the chicken, toss in the lemon juice and saute in the olive oil until beginning to brown.
2   Chop the onions, press the garlic and add these to the chicken. Sweat for a further 5 mins.
3   Slice the green pepper, dissolve the creamed coconut in the boiling water and skin and chop the tomatoes. Add to the pan along with the ground almonds and black pepper.
4   Stir, bring to the boil and simmer for 15 mins.
5   Add the parsley and serve with plain boiled rice.

CHICKEN CASSEROLE (4)

1 onion
2 oz mushrooms
(optional)
1 stick celery
1/4 green pepper
2 carrots
1 clove garlic
1/2 pt water
1 tsp cornflour

1 dsp tomato puree
(optional)
1/4 tsp marjoram
1/4 tsp rosemary
1/2 tsp paprika
1 bayleaf
1/4 tsp sage
black pepper
4 chicken joints (skinned)

1   Cut the vegetables into bite sized pieces and add to the casserole along with the pressed garlic.
2   Mix together the water, tomato puree, herbs and seasoning and pour over the vegetables.
3   Add the chicken pieces, cover the casserole and cook at reg 6, 200c, 400f for approx 1 1/4 hrs or until the chicken is tender.
4   Stir the cornflour in a little water and add to the casserole to thicken it. Re-heat and remove the bayleaf.
5   Serve with rice and a green salad or fresh vegetables.

STIR FRIED CHICKEN AND VEGETABLES (4)

Select 3-4 vegetables

2 courgettes	2 chicken breasts
1/2 red pepper	1/2 pt stock or water
4 oz mangetout	1 onion, sliced
2 carrots	1 tblsp olive oil
8 baby sweetcorn	1 clove garlic, pressed
2 oz water chestnuts	black pepper
4 oz broccoli	2 rounded tsp cornflour
2oz mushrooms	

1   Cut the vegetables into pieces which will cook in approx the same amount of time.
2   Sweat the onion and garlic in the olive oil for a few mins. Add the rest of the vegetables and the chicken and sweat for 5 mins.
3   Mix the stock to a smooth paste with the cornflour and add to the vegetables and meat.
4   Bring to the boil and simmer for approx 5 mins until the vegetables and chicken are cooked.
5   Season with black pepper and serve with boiled rice and salads.

An alternative sauce can be made for those allowed the following, by mixing one dsp tomato puree, one dsp light miso and two dsp shoyu sauce with 1/2 pt of water. Add this instead of the stock and cornflour.

CHICKEN WITH BARBECUE SAUCE (4)

2 tblsp lemon juice	1 clove garlic, pressed
2 tblsp tomato puree	1/4 pt apple juice
1 tsp chinese five	1/4 pt stock
spice powder	2 rounded tsps cornflour
4 chicken breasts	

1   Mix all the ingredients except the chicken and the cornflour to form a smooth sauce. Marinade the chicken in the sauce for at least 2 hrs.
2   Remove the chicken from the marinade, place on a greased baking tray in the centre of the oven at reg 6, 200c, 400f for 1/2 hr. Baste with the juices from the chicken once during cooking.
3   Mix the cornflour to a smooth paste in a pan with a little of the marinade. Add the remaining marinade and any juices from the cooked chicken. Bring to the boil, stirring constantly and allow to simmer for 2 mins.
4   Serve the chicken on a bed of rice with the sauce poured over.

SPICY BAKED CHICKEN (4)

2 cloves garlic	1 heaped tsp ground cumin
4 tblsp lemon juice	1 heaped tsp paprika
1/4 tsp black pepper	1 heaped tsp tumeric
4 chicken breasts or	1/4 tsp cayenne pepper
skinned portions	parsley to garnish

1   Combine all the ingredients except the chicken. Rub the spice mixture into the chicken pieces and leave to marinade for at least 3 hrs in a covered container.
2   Place the chicken pieces on a baking tray, cover with foil and bake in the centre of the oven at reg 6, 200c, 400f for 1/2 hr if using chicken breasts and 1 hr if using joints.
3   Serve sprinkled with parsley, accompanied by brown rice and dahl (see sauces) and with a salad or fresh vegetables.

If allowed a little yogurt could be mixed with any cooking juices from the chicken and served to accompany.
Use foil to cover the baking tray to make washing up easier.

SIMA'S CHICKEN (4)

8 oz brown rice
12 oz cooked chicken
3 tblsp raisins
black pepper

2 carrots
rind of 1/2 orange
juice of 1 orange
4 oz toasted flaked almonds

1   Cook the brown rice and keep warm.
2   Cut the chicken into bite sized pieces or into small joints.
3   Cut the carrots into matchstick pieces. Thinly pare the orange rind and cut into matchstick strips.
4   Cook the carrots in the orange juice, with the orange rind and raisins for approx 5 mins until just cooked. Warm the chicken.
5   Layer half of the rice, chicken, carrot mixture and nuts on a serving dish, then layer the remaining ingredients in the same way. Pour over any remaining cooking liquid from the carrots. If using chicken joints the rest of the ingredients can be layered and the chicken served round the edge of the plate.

CHICKEN LIVER RISOTTO (4)

7 oz brown rice
3 med onions
1 tblsp olive oil
black pepper

8 oz mushrooms
8 oz chicken livers
1/2 tsp basil

1   Cook the rice and keep warm.
2   Chop the onions, slice the mushrooms and cut the chicken livers into small pieces.
3   Sweat the onions in the oil in a lge frying pan or wok until they begin to soften and brown.
4   Turn the heat full on, add the mushrooms and stir fry for 2 mins.
5   Add the chicken livers, black pepper and basil and stir fry until the mixture begins to brown and the liver is just cooked. This will only take a few minutes.
6   Add the rice, mix well and serve.

Serve with vegetables and salads. Use organic chicken livers if possible.

RABBIT OR CHICKEN WITH PRUNES (4)

4 rabbit or chicken portions
1 dsp paprika
1 1/2 tsps sage
1 tsp thyme
1/4 tsp chilli powder
1 bayleaf
2 tsps lemon juice
1 dsp tomato puree
black pepper

2 onions, chopped
2 lge sticks celery, sliced
2 oz sliced mushrooms or
1 carrot cut into matchsticks
3/4 pt water or stock which
includes prune soaking liquid
2 tsps cornflour

1 Mix the paprika, sage, thyme and chilli. Skin the meat and toss in the spices until it is coated all over. Place in a casserole dish.
2 Mix the tomato puree with the stock and the lemon juice and add to the casserole along with the vegetables, prunes, pepper and bayleaf.
3 Cook slowly in the oven at reg 4, 185c, 370f for approx 2 hrs
4 Mix the cornflour with a little water and pour into the casserole whilst stirring. Bring to the boil and cook for 2 mins before serving.

Accompany with brown rice, millet or quinoa and with salads or vegetables.

LAMB WITH ORANGE AND GINGER SAUCE (4)

1 dsp tomato puree
1 tsp grated ginger
1/2 tsp dried ginger
1/4 tsp black pepper
1/2 tsp tumeric
1 tsp paprika
2 rounded tsp cornflour

juice 1 orange
grated rind 1 orange
2 cloves garlic, pressed
1/2 pt water
1 1/4 lb cubed lean lamb
2 med onions, diced

1   Mix the liquids and flavourings together in a casserole dish until
     smooth and well mixed.
2   Add the cubes of lamb and the onions and mix again.
3   Cook in the centre of the oven at reg 6, 200c, 400f for approx
     11/2 hrs or until the meat is tender.
4   Mix the cornflour with a little water and stir into the casserole.
     Bring to the boil and simmer for 2 mins.
5   Serve with brown rice and vegetables or salads.

LAMB KEBABS (4)

11/4 lb lean lamb
1 onion
8 med mushrooms or
1 lge pepper
1/2 tsp ground ginger
1/4 tsp black pepper

1 clove garlic, pressed
1 tblsp lemon juice
1 tblsp tomato puree
2 tblsp olive oil
1 tsp paprika

1   Mix all the ingredients except the lamb and vegetables to form a
     marinade. Cube the lamb and toss in the marinade. Leave to
     stand for at least 2 hrs, preferably longer.
2   Cut the onion into quarters and separate each quarter into its
     layers (a large piece of onion will not cook in the time it takes to
     cook the meat) If using the pepper cut into eight pieces.
3   Thread the meat, mushrooms or pepper and the onion layers
     onto 4 large skewers. Brush the vegetables with the marinade.
4   Place on a baking tray and bake at reg 6, 200c, 400f for 1/2 hr,
     turning once during cooking.
5   Serve with plain rice or nut pilau and salads.

LAMB KORMA WITH BANANAS (4)

5 onions	1 tsp garam masala
1 tblsp olive oil	1 tsp grated ginger
1 tsp ground coriander	2 cloves garlic, pressed
1/2 tsp ground cumin	1 dsp tomato puree, optional
1/2 tsp cardamom	2 oz creamed coconut
1/4 tsp ground cloves	3/4 pt boiling water
1/4 tsp cinnamon	1 tblsp raisins
1/2 tsp tumeric	2 bananas
1/4 tsp black pepper	1 1/4 lb lean lamb, cubed

1 Finely slice 3 onions and sweat in the olive oil over a gentle heat, stirring regularly until the onions are soft and a golden brown colour. This will take approx 30 mins.
2 Add the spices and the garlic and sweat for another few mins.
3 Place the onion mixture, the ginger and the tomato puree in a food processor and blend until very smooth.
4 Dissolve the creamed coconut in the boiling water in a large casserole dish. Add the onion mixture and the meat and mix well.
5 Roughly chop the two remaining onions and add to the casserole dish along with the raisins.
6 Place the casserole in the oven at reg 6, 200c, 400f, and cook for 11/2 hrs or until the meat is tender.
7 Cut the bananas into 1/2" lengths and add to the casserole just before serving. They only need a few minutes to warm through.

Serve with brown rice, millet or quinoa and with curry accompaniments, salads or vegetables.

If allowed stir 1/2 pt yogurt gradually into the korma just before serving

LAMB WITH NUT PILAU (4)

8 oz brown rice
1 dsp olive oil
1 med onion
2 cloves garlic
1 1/4 pts good stock
1 oz raisins
4 lamb chops

1/4 tsp cardamom
1 tsp ground cumin
1 tsp ground coriander
1/4 tsp tumeric
1/8 tsp chilli powder
1/2 tsp cinnamon
2 oz toasted split almonds

1   Soak the rice in lots of warm water for 20 mins. Rinse and drain
2   Finely chop the onion and press the garlic clove. Sweat the onion
    and garlic in the olive oil until they begin to soften and brown.
3   Add the rice and the spices and sweat for another few mins.
4   Add the stock and the raisins, bring to the boil, cover and
    simmer for approx 40-50 mins until the rice is cooked and all the
    liquid has been absorbed. To prevent the rice becoming too dry it
    may be necessary to add a little more water during cooking,
    especially towards the end.
5   Whilst the rice is cooking grill the chops.
6   Toss the almonds into the rice just before serving and serve with
    the chops on top.

Accompany with a salad or fresh vegetables.

FISH DISHES

COD PROVENCALE (4) ✳

1/2 tsp oregano
1/2 tsp basil
1/4 tsp thyme
1 tsp fennel seeds
1 bayleaf
black pepper
5 fl oz water

1 pt creamed tomatoes
  or tomato juice
1 onion, chopped
1 green pepper, diced
1 clove garlic, pressed
1 lb cod (thick piece)

1   Place the herbs, spices, water, tomatoes, vegetables and garlic
    into a pan and cook for 10 mins
2   Flake or cut the fish into bite sized pieces.
3   Add the fish to the tomato mixture and cook gently for 5 mins or
    until the fish is just cooked. Do not stir roughly or the fish will
    break up.
4   Serve on rice

This fish dish is so quick and easy to make yet it is delicious enough
to be used for entertaining. Try using salmon or monkfish instead of
the cod or add prawns or mussels as well. Serve sprinkled with lots
of fresh parsley.
If you cannot tolerate tomatoes try using carrot juice.

MACKEREL IN GINGER AND ORANGE (4)

juice 2 oranges
grated rind 1 orange
1 dsp tomato puree

4 mackerel fillets
1 tsp grated ginger
black pepper

1   Mix the orange juice, rind, ginger and tomato puree together.
2   Marinate the mackerel fillets in the mixture for at least 3 hrs.
3   Bake in a covered container in the marinade at reg 6, 200c, 400f
    for 20-25 mins or until the fish is just cooked.

Serve hot or cold with the juices poured over the fish.

FISH FLORENTINE (4)

1 lb spinach　　　　　*3/4 pt white sauce (see index)*
2 dsp ground nuts　　　*4 pieces fish ie. cod,*
　　　　　　　　　　　　haddock, salmon

1　Wash the spinach and cook in the water in which it has been washed for 3-5 mins until the spinach just falls but is not overcooked.
2　Drain the spinach and divide between four individual au gratin dishes.
3　Lay a piece of fish on each spinach bed.
4　Make the white sauce as directed and pour evenly over the fish. Sprinkle the nuts over the surface.
5　Bake for approx 15 mins near the top of the oven at reg 6, 200c, 400f, until the top is lightly brown and the fish is just cooked.

You could bake the fish altogether in a larger au gratin dish but extend the cooking time to approx 20-25 mins.

STIR FRY WITH PRAWNS AND PEACHES (4)

1 bunch spring onions　　*4 oz prawns*
2 carrots　　　　　　　　*4 oz toasted cashews*
1 dsp olive oil　　　　　*2 med peaches*
1 lb cooked rice　　　　*2 tblsp water*
black pepper

1　Finely slice the spring onions, cut the carrots into matchstick pieces and dice the peaches.
2　Sweat the carrots and spring onions in the olive oil until they just begin to soften.
3　Add the remaining ingredients and sweat until warmed through.

If allowed add 1 tblsp of shoyu sauce for extra flavour.
Note that prawns do contain salt unless freshly shelled.

PEPPERED COD (4)

4 cod fillets
2 tblsp olive oil
1 tblsp lemon juice
1/2 tsp paprika

2 tsp green peppercorns
2 tsp fresh chopped herbs ie.
parsley, tarragon, dill, fennel

1   Finely chop the peppercorns and mix along with the herbs into the oil and lemon juice.
2   Spread the mixture evenly over the cod fillets and sprinkle with the paprika.
3   Cook under a hot grill with the rack removed from the grillpan for approx 10 mins or until the fish is browning and just cooked. Do not turn over.

Serve with crisp stir fried vegetables, rice and salad.
Green peppercorns are available bottled in brine. You could however use dried green or black peppercorns soaked overnight in a little boiling water. Line the grill pan with foil to make washing up easier.

GRILLED FISH WITH TOMATO AND PESTO (4) ✳

4 pieces of fish
4 lge tomatoes
2 tsps pesto sauce
(see index)

4 dsp olive oil
4 dsp lemon juice
1 clove garlic, pressed
black pepper

1   Mix the oil, lemon juice and garlic. Pour over the fish and allow to marinade for at least 10 mins but longer if possible.
2   Skin and finely dice the tomatoes and mix with the pesto sauce and the pepper.
3   Cook the fish under a hot grill with the rack removed from the grill pan for approx 10 mins or until the fish is just cooked. Baste with the marinade during cooking.
4   Serve with the tomato and pesto mixture spread over the top of the fish.

It is best to use homemade pesto sauce as the bought varieties usually contain cheese.
Line the grill pan with foil to save on washing up.

FRIED FISH (4)

4 pieces filleted fish	*4 dsps cornmeal*
black pepper	*2 tblsp olive oil*

1   Mix the cornmeal and pepper on a plate
2   Wash the fish, dry a little with kitchen roll then dip into the cornmeal until the fish is well coated on both sides.
3   Fry the fish in the olive oil until it is golden brown on both sides and cooked through.

The cornmeal gives the fish a lovely golden colour but you can use soya flour if you cannot tolerate corn.

FISH PARCELS (4)

4 pieces fish	*1 tsp grated orange rind*
(preferably thick)	*juice 1 orange*
1 leek or	*1 tsp grated ginger*
4 spring onions	*2 tsps lemon juice*
1 carrot	*1 lge tomato*
1 stick celery	*black pepper*
1 sml courgette	*1 tblsp chopped parsley*

1   Place each piece of fish on a piece of foil approx 10" square.
2   Slice the leek or spring onions very finely, approx 1/8".
3   Cut the celery and carrot into very fine matchstick pieces.
4   Thinly slice the courgette.
5   Sprinkle the vegetables on top of the fish along with the parsley.
6   Mix the remaining ingredients together and pour over the fish and vegetables.
7   Lift the corners of the foil and twist to form parcels.
8   Place on a baking tray and bake at reg 6, 200c, 400f for approx 15-20 mins or until the fish is just cooked.

Serve on rice, millet or quinoa accompanied by salad or cooked vegetables.

FISH PIE (4) ✳

white sauce
2 level tblsp cornflour

1 lb cod or haddock
2 oz fresh or frozen peas
2 oz sweetcorn kernels
4 oz prawns
olive oil
2 lb potatoes

1/2 pt soya or almond milk
1/4 pt potato cooking water
black pepper
1/4 tsp nutmeg
1/2 tsp mustard
1 tsp lemon juice
1/2 tsp grated lemon rind
1 tblsp chopped parsley

1 Peel and chop the potatoes and boil in water until soft.
   Mash using a little of the cooking liquid to give a soft
   consistency and season with black pepper. Save the remaining
   cooking liquid to use in the white sauce.
2 To make the white sauce, mix the cornflour and mustard with a
   little milk in a saucepan. Add the rest of the milk, 1/4 pt of
   potato water and the remaining sauce ingredients. Bring to the
   boil stirring constantly then lower the heat and simmer for 2
   mins.
3 Cut the fish into small pieces and add to the sauce along with
   the prawns, peas and sweetcorn and mix gently.
4 Place the fish mixture into an au gratin dish and spread the
   mashed potato over the top.
5 Brush the surface with olive oil and bake near the top of the
   oven at reg 6, 200c, 400f for 30 mins. Place under a hot grill for
   a few minutes if the surface is not brown enough.

If allowed add a knob of butter to the mashed potatoes. If you cannot
tolerate potatoes try topping the fish pie with a mixture of mashed
parsnip and cooked millet mixed together. Prawns do contain salt
unless freshly cooked and shelled but another fish or vegetable could
be used instead.

SEAFOOD PASTA (4) ✳

Follow the above recipe but instead of topping with mashed potatoes
mix the fish sauce with 8 oz cooked pasta, made from rice, corn or
buckwheat.

STUFFED BAKED COD STEAKS (4)

1/2 sml onion
4 cod steaks
black pepper
1/2 beaten egg
4 tblsp cooked brown rice

2 tblsp sweetcorn or peas
1 tsp fresh chopped coriander
1 tblsp chopped fresh parsley
1/2 tsp grated lemon rind

1   Finely dice the onion and cook in 2 tblsp water until soft.
2   Remove the bones from the cod using a sharp knife and taking care to keep the steak in one piece.
3   Place the rice in a food processor with the egg and blend for a few seconds until well mixed but not completely smooth.
4   Mash the sweetcorn or peas with the back of a fork in a mixing bowl. Add the rice and egg, chopped herbs, lemon rind, black pepper and the sieved onion. Mix well.
5   Place the cod steaks on a greased baking tray, fill the centre of each with the stuffing and reshape. Cover with foil and bake in the centre of the oven at reg 6, 200c, 400f for approx 30 mins, removing the foil for the last 10 mins of cooking.

TUNA AND LENTIL BAKE (4)

6 oz red split lentils
1 lge onion, diced
1 dsp olive oil
black pepper

2 lge eggs
1/4 pt soya or almond milk
7 oz can tuna in water
2 tblsp chopped nuts

1   Wash the lentils and bring to the boil in a pan with 1 pt of water. Simmer for 20-25 mins until the lentils are soft and most of the liquid has been absorbed.
2   Sweat the onion in the oil until it begins to soften.
3   Separate the eggs and beat the yolks and milk together. Whisk the egg whites until stiff.
4   Flake the tuna fish and include the juices from the tin
5   Combine the lentils, onion, tuna, egg, milk and pepper. Fold in the egg whites using a metal spoon.
6   Pour the mixture into a shallow, greased ovenproof dish, sprinkle the surface with the nuts and bake at reg 4, 180c, 350f for 30 mins or until the bake is set and brown.

KEDGEREE (4) ✳

8 oz brown rice	*Sauce*
2 lge onions,diced	*2 tblsp fish cooking liquid*
1 dsp olive oil	*1 tsp curry powder*
2 hard boiled eggs	*2 tblsp olive oil*
8 oz fresh fish	*4 tblsp mayonnaise or*
2 oz prawns	*soya yogurt*
1 tblsp fresh parsley	*1 tblsp lemon juice*
	1/2 tsp grated lemon rind

1   Cook the brown rice, sieve and keep warm.
2   Sweat the onions in the oil until they begin to soften and brown.
    Cut the eggs into rough dice.
3   Poach the fish in 2 tblsp water in a pan until just cooked. Flake
    the fish and remove any skin or bones.
4   Mix the rice, fish, prawns, eggs, onions and parsley
5   Make the sauce by blending the fish liquid with the curry
    powder and the oil. If available it is best to use a food processor
    in order to obtain a thick emulsion. Add the mayonnaise or
    yogurt and the lemon juice and rind.
6   Pour the sauce over the fish and rice and mix gently with a fork.

FISH CAKES (4) ✳

14 oz potatoes	*1 tblsp chopped parsley*
1 med onion	*2 tsps lemon juice*
7 oz can tuna fish	*black pepper*
(in water)	*1 hard boiled egg*
olive oil	

1   Cook the potatoes in boiling water until soft. Mash using the
    drained water from the tuna to give a soft consistency.
2   Finely dice the onion and cook in 2 tblsp of water until soft.
    Sieve to remove the water.
3   Chop the hard boiled egg and stir into the potatoes along with
    the onion, tuna, parsley, lemon juice and black pepper.
4   Shape into 8 cakes and place on a well greased baking tray.
    Brush the fish cakes with olive oil and cook on the top shelf of a
    hot oven at reg 8, 230c, 450f for approx 20 mins or until brown.

TUNA, BUTTERBEAN AND LEEK SAVOURY (4)

1 lb leeks
1 lge carrot
1/4 pt water
7 oz can tuna in water
8 oz cooked
butterbeans
1 tblsp chopped nuts

1/2 pt soya or almond milk
2 level tblsp cornflour
1/2 tsp grated lemon rind
1/4 tsp ground nutmeg
1 dsp fresh parsley
black pepper

1   Slice the leeks and cut the carrot into matchstick pieces. Cook in
    1/4 pt of water, sieve and save the cooking liquid.
2   Drain and flake the tuna fish saving the juices from the tin.
3   Make the milk up to 3/4 pt with the tuna and vegetable
    liquids. Add a little water if necessary.
4   Mix the milk and cornflour together in a pan until smooth.
    Bring to the boil stirring constantly and simmer for 2 mins
5   Mix all the ingredients except the nuts into the sauce, taking
    care when mixing the butterbeans so that they do not break up.
6   Place the mixture into one large or four small au gratin dishes.
    Sprinkle the surface with nuts and serve.

QUICK FISH CASSEROLE (4)

4 portions fish
cod, haddock, hake etc
1 carrot
1/2 onion
1 dsp olive oil
1/4 pt water

1 bayleaf
black pepper
1/4 pt soya or almond milk
2 tsps cornflour
4 tblsp frozen peas

1   Grate the carrot and onion and sweat in the olive oil for 3 mins.
2   Add the fish and turn to coat with the vegetables and oil. Add
    the water, the bayleaf and some black pepper. Cover the pan
    and cook gently until the fish is almost cooked, approx 15 mins.
3   Mix the cornflour and milk to a smooth paste and add to the pan
    mixing it with the juices and vegetables. Bring to the boil, add
    the frozen peas, cover and cook gently for another 5 mins.

Serve with rice, millet or quinoa and salad or vegetables.

MAJORCAN FISH CASSEROLE (4)

1 1/2 lb potatoes
(even sized)
1 lge onion
1 dsp olive oil
1 courgette
1/2 lb spinach
2 tblsps pine nuts
2 tblsps raisins

1 tin tomatoes in tomato juice
1/4 tsp thyme
1/4 tsp marjoram
1/2 tsp fennel seeds
black pepper
4 pieces cod or hake
olive oil for brushing
the surface

1   Boil the potatoes whole in their skins for approx 10-15 mins depending on the size of the potatoes. The potatoes should be slightly undercooked at this stage. Allow to cool.

2   Dice the onion and sweat in the olive oil until softening and beginning to brown. Dice the courgette, add to the pan and sweat the vegetables for a few more minutes.

3   Chop the spinach and add to the onion and courgette along with the pine nuts, raisins, tomatoes, herbs and pepper. Bring to the boil and simmer for 5 minutes.

4   Place the mixture into one large or four small au gratin dishes. Lay the fish pieces on top.

5   Skin the potatoes and then using a food processor or hand grater, grate the potatoes. Pile the grated potatoes on top of the fish, pressing down a little but leaving the surface rough.

6   Brush the surface with olive oil and bake at the top of the oven for approx 15 mins for the small dishes and 20 mins for the larger at reg 6, 200c, 400f. Place under a hot grill for 2 mins if the potatoes have not browned sufficiently in the oven.

SAUCES

FRENCH DRESSING

juice 1 orange	Choose 4 dried herbs
juice 1 lemon	1/2 tsp parsley
olive oil	1/2 tsp chives
1 heaped tsp	1/2 tsp dill seeds
mustard	1/2 tsp fennel seeds
1/2 tsp lemon rind	1/2 tsp celery seeds
1/2 tsp orange rind	1/2 tsp tarragon
black pepper	1/2 tsp mint

If substituting fresh herbs use 1 tsp of each.
Other flavourings which could be added include :-

1/2 tsp paprika	1/2 tsp grated ginger
1 tsp tomato puree	1 tsp grated raw onion
1 tsp tahini	1 clove garlic, pressed

1   Place the orange and lemon juice in a screw topped jar and add an equal amount of olive oil.
2   Add the remaining ingredients and shake well.
3   Store in the fridge ready for use.

If allowed, a tsp of honey makes this dressing taste less sharp. If you do not like the taste of olive oil, use half sunflower oil, but gradually keep reducing the amount as you become accustomed to the taste of olive oil. If you cannot tolerate citrus fruits but can tolerate cider vinegar, use 1/3 rd vinegar and 2/3 rds olive oil in the above recipe

TOFU MAYONNAISE

1 tblsp lemon juice	1 pkt (10oz) silken tofu
1/2 tsp mustard	6 fl oz oil (use a mixture
black pepper	of olive oil and sunflower)

1   Process the tofu, lemon juice, mustard and pepper.
2   Slowly add the oils through the funnel of the food processor with the machine on full power.
3   Store the mayonnaise in the fridge in a covered container. Flavour with garlic, curry powder, tomato puree, spring onion or herbs if desired.

MAYONNAISE

1 tblsp lemon juice   **2 egg yolks + 1 tblsp water**
1 lge tsp mustard   **OR 1 whole egg**
black pepper   **approx 6 fl oz oil (use a**
                         mixture of olive + sunflower)

1   Process all the ingredients except the oil until well mixed.
2   Leave the food processor running on high power and **VERY**
     slowly add the oil a few drops at a time until it starts to
     emulsify. Then add the rest of the oil slowly until the desired
     thickness of mayonnaise is obtained.
3   Store in the fridge and use as required.

The amount of oil varies according to the size of the eggs. I never
measure the oil but just pour it from the bottle until the mayonnaise
is the right thickness. Just olive oil can be used but this produces
quite a strong flavoured mayonnaise.

Vary the mayonnaise by adding flavourings such as herbs, garlic,
curry powder, tomato puree or spring onions.

THOUSAND ISLANDS MAYONNAISE

Add the following ingredients to the above mayonnaise and mix :-

2 tblsp chopped green olives
2 tsp finely chopped parsley
2 tsp finely chopped onions or chives
2 tsp tomato puree
2 tblsp finely chopped green pepper.

WHITE SAUCE

1/2 tsp lemon rind
1/4 tsp nutmeg
black pepper

3/4 pt soya or almond milk
2 level tblsp cornflour
1 level tsp mustard
1 bayleaf

1   Mix the cornflour, mustard and a little milk together in a
     saucepan until smooth.
2   Add the remaining milk along with the lemon rind, nutmeg,
     bayleaf and black pepper.
3   Bring to the boil stirring constantly. Simmer for 2 mins
4   Remove the bayleaf.

PARSLEY SAUCE
Add 2 tblsp finely chopped parsley to the above sauce

ONION SAUCE
Boil a finely diced onion in 1/4 pt water until soft. Drain, keep the
liquid and use this instead of some of the milk in the above recipe.
Add the onions to the cooked sauce along with lots of black pepper
and the other ingredients.

MUSHROOM SAUCE
Add 1/4 lb sliced and sauteed mushrooms to the sauce.

VELOUTE SAUCE
Use a good quality stock instead of half of the milk in the above
recipe.

PESTO SAUCE

1oz pine nuts
2 fl oz olive oil
black pepper

2oz fresh basil leaves
1 clove garlic, pressed

1   Using a pestle and mortar or food processor, blend the basil,
     pine nuts and garlic thoroughly, then gradually work in the olive
     oil to give a smooth mixture.
2   Store in the fridge.

HERB AND WALNUT SAUCE

Substitute walnuts for the pine nuts in the pesto sauce recipe and a selection of herbs such as parsley, mint, chives, tarragon, coriander and dill instead of the basil leaves.

Serve a teaspoonful mixed into a bowl of freshly boiled rice for a delicious snack. Pesto sauce can also be used to add flavour to risottos, soups and casseroles.

RATATOUILLE SAUCE

1/2 aubergine	1 lge tin chopped tomatoes
2 courgettes	in tomato juice
1/2 green pepper	1/2 pt water
1/2 red pepper	1/2 tsp basil
1 lge onion	1/2 tsp oregano

1   Dice the aubergine and peppers and slice the courgettes and onion.
2   Place all the ingredients into a saucepan and bring to the boil . Cover the pan and simmer for 40 mins.

Serve as a sauce or vegetable accompaniment.

FRESH TOMATO SAUCE

1 clove garlic, pressed	1 lb tomatoes
1 dsp olive oil	2 tblsp chopped fresh herbs black
pepper	ie. parsley, chives, basil,
	coriander, marjoram.

1   Place the oil in a saucepan and sweat the garlic for a few mins.
2   Skin and chop the tomatoes and add to the pan
3   Add the remaining ingredients and cook until the tomatoes have just melted, no more than 5 mins.

Serve immediately with nut roasts, vegetables, rice etc

VEGETABLE PUREE SAUCE

1 med onion	4 lge carrots
2 lge tomatoes	1/2 pt water
1 tsp lemon juice	black pepper

1   Dice the onion and slice the carrots. Skin the tomatoes.
2   Cook the onion and carrot in the water until they are just soft, then allow to cool slightly.
3   Process the carrot, onion and water until smooth. Add the tomatoes, lemon juice and pepper and process again.
4   Heat through but do not cook further.

Serve with nut roasts, rice, fish or chicken. Fresh herbs could be added if desired ie. parsley, chives, basil, coriander, marjoram.

DAHL

7 oz red split lentils	1/2 tsp ground coriander
13/4 pt water	1/2 tsp tumeric
1 tsp grated ginger	1 tsp cumin seeds
1 clove garlic	1/4 tsp cayenne pepper
	1/2 tsp garam masala

1   Wash the lentils, press the garlic clove and place all the ingredients into a saucepan. Bring to the boil.
2   Simmer gently, stirring occasionally for 1 1/2 hrs

Use as a sauce for vegetarian roasts, or on its own with brown rice or spicy baked chicken. If allowed add 2 tblsp of yogurt just before serving.

A variation on the above can be made by substituting whole green lentils instead of the red lentils and adding a finely diced onion. This dish is ideal to serve along with a meat dish and a vegetarian dish as part of an Indian style meal.

CURRY SAUCE

1 lge onion
1 dsp olive oil
1 lge baking apple
1 tsp curry powder
1 1/2 pts water

2 oz red split lentils
1 oz creamed coconut
2 tblsp raisins
1 tblsp tomato puree
(optional)

1   Dice the onion and grate the baking apple. Sweat the onion in
    the oil until it begins to soften and brown.
2   Add the grated apple and the curry powder and sweat for a few
    more mins.
3   Add the remaining ingredients, bring to the boil and simmer
    covered for at least 1 hr until the lentils and apples have become
    part of a thick sauce. Stir occasionally during cooking and add a
    little more water if the sauce is too dry.

Serve as a sauce to add flavour to rice, meat or vegetables. A
vegetable curry can be made by adding 1lb of chopped mixed
vegetables and cooking in the sauce until tender. Alternatively make
an egg curry by hardboiling one egg per person and serving the egg
halved, on top of rice with the sauce poured over.

CHICK PEA AND AVOCADO SAUCE

1 med avocado
1 tblsp lemon juice
3 tblsp water

1 tblsp tahini
1 tblsp olive oil
4 oz cooked chick peas

1   Process the avocado with the lemon juice, water and olive oil.
2   Add the remaining ingredients and process until a smooth sauce
    is obtained.

Use as a sauce with rice, nut roasts, vegetables etc or as a dip with
vegetable crudities. Add more water if a softer sauce is required.

FENNEL AND CASHEW NUT SAUCE

8 oz leeks
8 oz fennel
1/4 pt water or stock
1/4 pt soya or almond milk

1/2 tsp fennel seeds
1/2 tsp grated ginger
1 oz cashew nuts
black pepper

1 Slice the leeks using mainly the white stems and dice the fennel.
2 Bring these to the boil in the water or stock, add the fennel seeds, the ginger and the pepper and simmer for 10 mins.
3 Process the cashew nuts until fine, then add the leek and fennel mixture and process again until the sauce is smooth and creamy.
4 Return to the pan along with the milk, bring the sauce to the boil and serve.

Serve with rice, millet, quinoa or pasta.

PEA AND CARAWAY SAUCE

6 oz whole peas
1 tsp caraway seeds

7 fl oz water
black pepper

1 Soak the peas overnight in lots of water. Rinse the peas, cover with boiling water, bring to the boil and cook the peas until soft (this will only take approx 10 mins in a pressure cooker).
2 Drain off the excess liquid. Using this liquid and some extra water if necessary, measure out 7 fl oz and add this to the peas along with the pepper and caraway seeds.
3 Bring to the boil and simmer until the peas fall to form a sauce. Add a little more water if needed

BAKING WITHOUT

Because the baked goods in this section contain very little fat and no sugar they will not keep for too long. Store in the fridge and eat within three days. They may be cut into slices, or packed in small portions and stored in the freezer to be used as needed.If you cannot tolerate eggs then you will find a variety of egg replacers available in health food shops or alternatively make your own by following the recipe in the ingredients section of this book. Egg replacers will help to bind ingredients together but do not help mixtures to rise as do ordinary eggs. It may be necessary to add an extra 1/2 tsp baking powder in cakes and breads where a light texture is desired.

Potassium baking powder is also available in health food shops and is used in place of ordinary baking powder in these recipes to avoid the use of excess sodium. If you cannot find either potassium baking powder or egg replacer in your health food shop then do ask as these are available from the wholesalers but may not have been asked for before.

I have tried to use the more readily available flours but others could be substituted. The range is continually increasing. Do experiment with other flours if you cannot use the ones suggested. Also try using alternative flours instead of wheat flour in some of your favourite recipes.

For 1 cup wheat flour substitute :- 3/4 cup cornmeal, 3/8 cup potato flour, 1 1/2 cups sago flour, 7/8 cup buckwheat flour, 7/8 cup rice flour and 3/4 cup soya flour.

FRUIT AND NUT SLICES

1 lge carrot   *8 oz well cooked brown rice*
1 med apple   *2 eggs or egg replacer*
4 oz rice flour   *2 oz hazelnuts*
2 fl oz water   *2 oz raisins*
1/2 tsp cinnamon   *sesame or sunflower seeds*
1/2 tsp nutmeg   *to decorate*

1   Line a shallow tin (approx 12"by 9") with greaseproof paper or foil and oil the surface.

2   Roughly chop the carrot and apple and place in a food processor with the rice flour, water, spices, cooked rice and eggs. Process until fairly smooth.

3   Add the fruit and nuts and process for approx 10 secs until the fruit and nuts are chopped a little but still in pieces.

4   Place the mixture into the prepared tin and smooth the surface. Mark into 16 sections and sprinkle the surface with sunflower or sesame seeds.

5   Bake at reg 6, 200c, 400f for 20 mins.

6   Cool in the tin, then turn the slices over and peel off the paper or foil.

7   Store in an airtight container in the fridge and use within 3 days. Alternatively pack in handy sized portions and freeze ready for snacks to take to work or on outings.

If you do not have a food processor, grate the carrot and apple finely and chop the nuts, then mix all the ingredients together. This produces a slice which is more chunky and chewy. These slices benefit from the rice being well cooked and are ideal to make with an overcooked batch. Cooked millet or quinoa can be used instead of rice. A baking or an eating apple can be used.

PARSNIP, BANANA AND APRICOT SLICES

Use the above recipe but substitute the carrot with a parsnip, the raisins with chopped dried apricots and add 2 oz banana to the mixture before processing.

CAROB SLICES

1 lge carrot
1 med apple
2 oz carob flour
2 oz rice flour ·
2 fl oz water
sunflower seeds
to decorate

8 oz well cooked brown rice
2 eggs or egg replacer
1/2 tsp mixed spice
1 oz desiccated coconut
2 oz raisins
2 oz hazelnuts

1 Line a shallow tin (approx 12" by 9") with greaseproof paper or foil and oil the surface.
2 Roughly chop the carrot and apple and place in a food processor along with the carob flour, rice flour, water, cooked rice, eggs and mixed spice. Process until well mixed and fairly smooth.
3 Add the coconut, raisins and hazelnuts and process for 10 secs until the nuts and fruit are chopped a little but are still in pieces.
4 Place the mixture in the prepared tin and smooth the surface. Mark into 16 sections and sprinkle the surface with sunflower seeds.
5 Bake at reg 6, 200c, 400f for 20 mins.
6 Allow to cool in the tin, turn the slices over and peel off the paper or foil. Store in an airtight container in the fridge and use within 3 days or pack in small portions in the freezer.

Carob slices, the fruit and nut slices and the savoury slices are all based on the same recipe which was invented by a patient of mine who had young children on this dietary regime. She wanted them to be able to take something to school for breaktime which seemed an acceptable snack food. I make batches twice per week and keep them in the fridge. There is then always something to take to work, on outings or to nibble whenever a snack is needed.

SAVOURY SLICES

1 lge carrot	8 oz well cooked brown rice
1 med apple	2 eggs or egg replacer
4 oz rice flour	2oz sweetcorn kernels
2 fl oz water	4 sundried tomatoes
1/4 tsp chilli powder	8 olives quartered
1 tsp fennel seeds	2 oz sunflower or pumpkin seeds
1/2 tsp dried tarragon	black pepper
	sesame or poppy seeds to garnish

1   Line a shallow tin, approx 12" by 9" with foil or greased proof
     paper. Oil the surface.
2   Roughly chop the carrot and apple and place in a food processor
     with the rice flour, water, herbs and spices, the cooked brown
     rice and the eggs. Process until well mixed and fairly smooth.
3   Tip the mixture out into a bowl and mix in the sunflower or
     pumpkin seeds, the sweetcorn, the finely chopped sun dried
     tomatoes and the olives.
4   Spread into the prepared tin and smooth the surface. Mark into
     16 sections and sprinkle the surface with sesame or poppy seeds
     and lots of freshly ground black pepper.
5   Bake at reg 6, 200c, 400f for 20 mins
6   Allow to cool in the tin then turn the slices over and peel off the
     paper or foil. Store in an airtight container in the fridge and eat
     within 3 days or freeze and use as needed.

If the sundried tomatoes are not in olive oil soak first in a little
water to soften. Use a baking or an eating apple.

APPLE, DATE AND NUT MUFFINS

8 oz cooking apple	*8 oz brown rice flour*
weighed after peeling	*2 rounded tsps potassium B.P.*
2 oz chopped walnuts	*1 tblsp sunflower oil*
2 oz sultanas	*1 egg or egg replacer*
2oz chopped dates	*8 fl oz water*
1/4 tsp cinnamon	
1/4 tsp nutmeg	

1. Cut the apple into 1/2" dice and place in a bowl with the fruit and nuts.
2. Place the remaining ingredients in a food processor and process until smooth. If you do not have a processor, beat together in a bowl.
3. Combine the two sets of ingredients.
4. Pile into 12 greased bun or muffin tins. The mixture will be piled up high if using bun tins but this will be fine.
5. Bake for approx 20 mins at reg 6, 200c, 400f .
6. Remove from the tins and place on a wire tray to cool.
   Store in the fridge and eat within 3 days. They can be frozen if desired.

These muffins are delicious and a real treat for anyone who misses cakes. Do not however overeat as they are high in fruit sugar especially if you have candida problems.

The mixture can be cooked as a loaf by placing in a greased and lined loaf tin and baking for 1 1/4 hrs at reg 4, 180c, 350f. Remove from the tin, peel off the lining paper and cool on a wire tray.

BANANA, DATE AND NUT LOAF

Substitute 8 oz of chopped banana instead of the apple in the above recipe.

GINGER AND ORANGE CAKE

4 oz potato flour

2 oz rice flour

2 oz ground almonds

1 tblsp sunflower oil

2 oz banana

3 oz sultanas

juice of 1 orange made up to

6 fl oz with water

1 tsp grated orange rind

1 tsp ground ginger

2 heaped tsp potassium B.P.

1 egg or an egg replacer and

an extra 2 fl oz water

1   If a food processor is available place all the ingredients except the dried fruit into the goblet and process until smooth and well mixed. Alternatively, beat the egg in a bowl and add the remaining ingredients beating well with a wooden spoon.

2   Add and mix in the sultanas.

3   Place the mixture in a small greased loaf tin and bake in the centre of the oven at reg 6, 200c, 400f for approx 30 mins or until golden brown and firm to the touch.

4   Turn out of the tin and cool on a wire tray. Keep in a covered container in the fridge and eat within 3 days.

If allowed add crystallised ginger and candied peel instead of 2 oz sultanas for a really delicious but not too sinful cake.

CARROT AND COCONUT CAKE

1/2 tsp nutmeg

1/2 tsp cinnamon

1 tblsp sunflower oil

6 fl oz warm water

3 oz sultanas

5 oz brown rice flour

6 oz finely grated carrot

2 heaped tsp potassium B.P.

1 egg or an egg replacer and

an extra 2 fl oz water

2 oz desiccated coconut

1   If a processor is available blend all the ingredients except the sultanas until smooth and well mixed. If a processor is not available beat the egg in a bowl, add the other ingredients and beat well with a wooden spoon. Add and mix in the sultanas.

2   Place the mixture in a small greased loaf tin and bake in the centre of the oven at reg 6, 200c, 400f for approx 40 mins or until firm to the touch and golden brown. Cool on a wire tray.

POTATO FLOUR BREAD

4 oz potato flour
2 oz rice flour
2 oz soya flour
6 fl oz warm water

1 egg or an egg replacer and
an extra 2 fl oz water
1 tblsp sunflower oil
2 rounded tsp potassium B.P.

1   If a processor is available, place all the ingredients into the goblet and process until smooth and well mixed. If not available, beat the egg in a bowl and add the remaining ingredients beating well with a wooden spoon.
2   Place in a small greased loaf tin and bake at reg 6, 200c, 400f for 30-35 mins or until firm to the touch and golden brown in colour.
3   Remove from the tin and cool on a wire tray. Store in an airtight container in the fridge and eat within 3 days.

CORNBREAD

4 oz med maize meal
2 oz potato flour
1/2 sml baking apple
1 tblsp sunflower oil

1 egg or an egg replacer
and an extra 2 fl oz water
4 fl oz warm water
2 rounded tsp potassium B.P.

1   Mix all the ingredients together in a food processor or if mixing by hand beat the egg and grate the apple, then beat in the remaining ingredients with a wooden spoon.
2   Place in a small greased loaf tin and bake at reg 6, 200c, 400f for 35 mins.
3   Remove from the tin, cool on a wire tray and store in the fridge in an airtight container. Eat within 3 days.

ONION AND HERB LOAF

4 oz rice flour	1 level tsp mustard
2 oz maize meal	2 heaped tsp potassium B.P.
2 oz soya flour	1 tblsp olive oil
1 tsp dried parsley	11 fl oz warm water OR
1/4 tsp thyme	9 fl oz plus 1 egg
1/2 tsp sage	2 spring onions or
	1 tblsp minced onion

1   If using a food processor place all the ingredients in the goblet and process until smooth and well mixed. If mixing by hand place the mustard in a bowl and beat with a little water until smooth. Add the remaining ingredients and beat well with a wooden spoon.
2   Place the mixture in a small greased loaf tin and bake in the centre of the oven at reg 6, 200c, 400f for approx 40 mins until the loaf is brown and firm to the touch.
3   Remove from the tin and cool on a wire tray. Store in the fridge in an airtight container and eat within 3 days.

ONION AND HERB FOCACCIA BREAD

1 small onion	herb and onion loaf mixture
2 cloves garlic	(as above)
1 tblsp olive oil	2 tblsp fresh chopped herbs
8 olives, optional	ie. thyme, marjoram, parsley,
3 sundried tomatoes	rosemary, chives.

1   Cut the onion in half and slice into paper thin slices. Place in a bowl and mix to coat with the olive oil.
2   Cut the garlic into very thin slices and the olives in half
3   Cut the sundried tomatoes into small pieces.
4   Grease two baking trays. Make the herb and onion loaf mixture and spread into two 9" rounds on the trays
5   Spread the onion, garlic, olives, tomatoes and herbs over the surface and bake near the top of the oven at reg 6, 200c, 400f for 25-30 mins until the bread is quite brown and crisp. Serve whilst still hot with salads or soup

SPICED CARROT BREAD

5 oz rice flour
or millet flour
1/2 tsp nutmeg
1/2 tsp cinnamon
3 fl oz warm water

1 egg or egg replacer
+ an extra 2 fl oz water
6 oz finely grated carrot
2 heaped tsp potassium B.P.
1 tblsp sunflower oil

1   If a processor is available, place all the ingredients into the
    goblet and process until they are well mixed and smooth. If
    unavailable, beat the egg in a bowl and add the remaining
    ingredients beating well with a wooden spoon.
2   Place the mixture in a small greased loaf tin and bake for
    approx 35-40 mins at reg 6, 200c, 400f, or until firm to the touch
    and beginning to brown.
3   Turn out onto a wire tray to cool. Store in an airtight container
    in the fridge and eat within 3 days.

ALMOND AND SOYA BISCUITS

1 1/2 oz soya flour
4 oz ground almonds

4 level tblsp carrot puree
sunflower seeds to decorate

1   Cook a medium sized carrot until tender. Process to form a
    smooth puree, then measure out 4 tblsp of the puree.
2   Mix the carrot puree, soya flour and ground almonds in a food
    processor until you have a thick, sticky mixture.
3   Press together any loose pieces and roll out by hand into a
    sausage shape, approx 1" in diameter. Use a little soya flour if
    necessary to stop the mixture sticking.
4   Cut into thin slices, approx 1/8" thick using a sharp knife. There
    should be approx 30 slices.
5   Lay the biscuits on a greased baking sheet. Press a few
    sunflower seeds into the surface of each biscuit.
6   Bake at reg 4, 180c, 350f for 20 mins until beginning to brown
    and crisp around the edges.
7   Cool on a wire tray and then store in an airtight container and
    eat within 3 days.

CHEWY FRUIT BARS

4 oz dried apricots
4 oz ground almonds
2 oz desiccated coconut
2 oz nuts ie almonds
2 oz dried fruit ie
raisins, apple, peach

4 fl oz orange juice or water
1 tsp grated orange rind
2 oz puffed rice cakes
or puffed rice cereal
Extra desiccated coconut

1 Cut the apricots into small pieces and simmer in the orange
   juice and orange rind or water until soft, approx 5 mins.
2 Chop the nuts into small pieces and toast in the oven or under
   the grill. Toast the desiccated coconut in the same way but
   watch whilst they all toast or they will soon burn.
3 Break the puffed rice cakes into pieces and place in the food
   processor goblet. Add the coconut, the ground almonds, the
   apricot mixture and process until well mixed. You will need to
   stop the machine and scrape the mixture from the sides of the
   bowl once or twice as the mixture is quite sticky.
4 Turn the mixture out into a bowl and add the chopped toasted
   nuts and the chopped dried fruit. Mix by hand until the mixture
   forms a large ball.
5 Line a baking tray with foil or greased proof paper and sprinkle
   with desiccated coconut. Spread the mixture out levelling the
   surface and sprinkle with more coconut. Press it down well. Cut
   into 12 or 16 pieces then leave to dry out, preferably overnight
   before storing in an airtight container. Use within 1 week.

POPCORN

3 tblsp popcorn

Method 1 :-Place the popcorn in a large bowl and cover with a large
plate. Microwave on the highest setting for approx 5 mins until the
popcorn has stopped popping .

Method 2 :-Heat a dsp of olive oil in a heavy bottomed pan until hot.
Add the corn, cover the pan with a lid and keep on a high heat until
the corn has finished popping. Shake the pan regularly to prevent
the corn sticking and burning.

CAROB BIRTHDAY CAKE

This cake contains rather too much oil to eat on a daily basis but enables one to celebrate special occasions without feeling the odd one out

2 oz banana	*2 eggs*
2 oz carob flour	*2 heaped tsps potassium B.P.*
1 1/2 oz potato flour	*4 oz sunflower oil*
2 1/2 oz rice flour	*7 tblsp soya milk or water*

1   If a processor is available process all the ingredients until smooth and well mixed. If you do not have a processor, mash the banana well then add the beaten eggs and the remaining ingredients beating well with a wooden spoon. Sieve the carob flour if it is lumpy.

2   Place in a greased lined 7" sandwich tin and bake in the middle of the oven at reg 3, 170c, 330f for 50-60 mins. Do not undercook or the cake will tend to deflate on cooling.

3   Turn out onto a wire tray and cool.

When cool cut the cake into 3 layers and sandwich together with carob cream which has been made with 4 fl oz water instead of 5 fl oz (see index). Top with carob cream and decorate with toasted nuts or desiccated coconut. Carob chocolate could be used to decorate the cake but check the ingredients first.

The above mixture can be made into 12 deep buns which will need cooking for approx 20 mins. The potato flour can be omitted and extra rice flour used if desired. An egg replacer does not substitute well in this recipe as it is difficult to make a light cake without eggs. If you do use, add an extra tsp potassium B.P.

CHRISTMAS CAKE

This cake contains too much oil to be eaten too often but is delicious for special occasions. Salt free butter can be used to replace the oil.

6 oz dried dates
5 fl oz water
4 oz sunflower oil
1 oz ground almonds
1 tsp mixed spice

3 eggs or egg replacer
2 oz rice flour
2 oz soya flour
2 oz fine maize flour
1 lb mixed dried fruit

1   Chop the dates into small pieces and place in a pan with the water. Bring to the boil and simmer over a low heat until the dates are soft (approx 10 mins). Cool.
2   Process or beat together the dates, oil, ground almonds, spices, eggs and flours until they are well blended.
3   Stir in the dried fruit and mix well by hand.
4   Place into a lined and greased 6-8" cake tin and bake at reg 3, 170c, 330f for approx 30 mins, then lower the temperature to reg 1, 145c, 290f for a further 45 mins

ALMOND PASTE

2oz dried dates
2 fl oz water

4 oz ground almonds
2 drops natural almond essence

1   Finely chop the dates and simmer in the water on a low heat until the dates are soft.
2   Process the dates, almonds and essence until the mixture starts to bind together. Press together any loose pieces and roll the mixture into a ball by hand.
3   Roll out the almond paste in rice flour to fit the Christmas cake. Decorate with nuts if desired.

SIMNEL CAKE

Use half the almond paste, roll out into a circle and sandwich in the middle of the Christmas cake mixture before cooking. Cook as above. When cool place the remaining almond paste on top.

MINCEMEAT

8 oz dried apricots	1 lb mixed dried fruit
1/2 tsp ground ginger	1 1/4 lb cooking apples
1/2 tsp nutmeg	grated rind 1 orange
1/2 tsp cinnamon	juice 1 lge orange
12 fl oz water	

1 Finely chop the dried apricots and grate the apples.
2 Put all the ingredients into a saucepan, bring to the boil and simmer gently for approx 20 mins, stirring occasionally to prevent sticking. Allow to cool.
3 Store in jars or tupperware containers for no more than 3 weeks in the fridge and up to 6 mths in the freezer.

MINCE PIES

Pastry Ingredients

1 oz ground almonds	3 tblsp water
3 oz rice flour	2 tblsp sunflower oil
1/4 tsp cinnamon	1 rounded dsp nut butter
1/8 tsp ground cloves	(almond, cashew, or hazelnut)

1 Place all the ingredients into the food processor and blend until well mixed. The mixture will still resemble breadcrumbs but will form into a pastry as you press it together by hand. If you do not have a processor, mix the dry ingredients together then mix the wet ingredients together. Combine the two sets of ingredients with a fork and then press together by hand.
2 Divide the pastry in half and roll out each half sandwiched between cling film. This helps to prevent the pastry from breaking.
3 At this point you can either wrestle with the pastry to make small mince pies or give in to the fact that the pastry is quite brittle and make a large plate pie. You may still have to patch the pie but do not worry it will taste fine.
4 Use the mincemeat to fill the pie or pies, cover with a pastry lid and press the pastry together at the edges.
5 Bake at reg 4, 180c, 350f for approx 10 mins for small pies and 15-20 mins for the large pie until golden brown and crisp.

DESSERTS

DESSERTS

I have tried to include a good selection of desserts, so that treats are available for weekends, for entertaining or for those evenings when you just feel like something special. However it has been necessary to include tropical fruits and acidic fruits in quite a few recipes in order to do this. As these should not be eaten too regularly try to eat starters rather than puddings on most days and save desserts for the occasional meal.

APRICOT AND BANANA CHEESE CAKE (4)

Base	Topping
1 1/2 oz hazelnuts	2 oz dried apricots
1 oz desiccated coconut	3 oz banana (after peeling)
1 rice cake or 2 tblsp	290 gm pkt firm silken tofu
puffed rice cereal	1/4 tsp cinnamon
hazelnuts to decorate	1/4 tsp grated lemon rind

To make the base
1   Toast the hazelnuts and coconut separately either in the oven or under the grill until golden brown in colour. Allow to cool then rub the skins off the hazelnuts.
2   Place all the base ingredients into a food processor and process until the nuts are finely chopped and all the ingredients are mixed. Remove from the processor.

To make the topping
1   Cut the apricots into small pieces and simmer in a small amount of water until soft. Sieve to remove the cooking liquid.
2   Process the apricots, banana, tofu, cinnamon and lemon rind until smooth

To assemble
Alternate two layers of both the base and topping ingredients (finishing with a layer of topping) either in a dish or preferably in four tall glasses or sundae dishes. Decorate with a few hazelnuts.

Tofu may need avoiding when initially treating candida.

CAROB CREAM (4)

4 oz cashew nuts   *2 lge bananas*
5 fl oz water   *1 tblsp carob powder*
toasted split almonds to decorate

1 Place all the ingredients in a food processor for 2 mins until
  smooth and creamy in texture.

Serve in sundae glasses with toasted split almonds to decorate or as
a topping for other deserts.

PRUNE SOUFFLE (4)

8 oz prunes   *grated rind 1 orange*
2" stick cinnamon or   *juice 1 orange made up*
1/2 tsp ground cinnamon   *1/2 pt with water*
4 egg whites

1   Place the prunes in a pan with the orange juice, water,
     cinnamon and orange rind. Bring to the boil and simmer for 5
     mins. Remove from the heat and leave to soak overnight.
2   Remove the cinnamon stick and the stones from the prunes.
     Blend the prunes in a food processor along with any remaining
     soaking liquid. Add a little water if necessary to obtain a fairly
     thick puree.
3   Beat the egg whites until very stiff and fold into the prune puree
     with a metal spoon.
4   Place in an oiled souffle dish or 4 individual dishes and bake at
     reg 6, 200c, 400f for approx 15 mins for the small souffles and
     25 mins for the larger. The souffle should be set and lightly
     brown in colour. Serve immediately.

Other dried fruit can be used instead of prunes ie. peaches, apricots.
Use the leftover egg yolks to make mayonnaise.

APRICOT MOUSSE (4)

8 oz dried apricots *1 sachet gelatine or gelozone*
3/4 pt water *2 eggs, separated*
1 tblsp lemon juice

1 Cut the apricots into small pieces and place in a saucepan with the water. Bring to the boil and simmer for 5 mins then allow to cool. The apricots should be quite soft.
2 Puree the apricots and sufficient of the cooking liquid to make a soft puree.
3 Dissolve the gelatine in 2 tblsp of water in a bowl over a pan of hot water. Add to the puree mixing well.
4 Add the 2 eggs yolks and the lemon juice and mix well. Leave the puree to cool until half set.
5 Whisk the egg whites in a bowl until stiff and fold into the half set puree mixture. Place in a jelly mould or serving dish and refrigerate until set.

ALMOND AND MINCEMEAT APPLES (4)

4 eating apples *2 tblsp flaked almonds*
4 tblsp mincemeat *3 fl oz apple juice*
(see index)

1 Peel, halve and core the apples and lay in a serving dish, core side uppermost.
2 Put 1/2 tblsp mincemeat in the centre of each apple and pour the apple juice around them.
3 Cover the dish and bake for 1/2 hr in the centre of the oven at reg 6, 200c, 400f.
4 Toast the flaked almonds and sprinkle over the surface before serving.

BAKED STUFFED APPLES (4)

4 eating apples
1/2 tsp mixed spice
1/2 tsp grated ginger
4 tblsp mixed dried fruit ie
apricots, raisins, dates

grated rind 1/2 orange
juice 1 orange or 3 fl oz
water

1   Wash and core the apples and place in a casserole dish which is not too large so that the apples are supported by the sides. Prick the skins with a knife to prevent them bursting.

2   Mix the chosen dried fruit (finely chopped if using larger fruits) with the grated orange rind, ginger and 1/4 tsp mixed spice.

3   Stuff the apples tightly with the fruit mixture and pour the orange juice or water into the casserole dish. Sprinkle the remaining mixed spice over the surface.

4   Cover the apples and bake in the centre of the oven at reg 6, 200c, 400f for approx 30 mins until the apples are just soft but not mushy.

Serve hot with vanilla custard, soya yogurt or just as they are.

RICE PUDDING (4)

4 oz brown rice flakes
1 stick cinnamon or
1/2 tsp ground cinnamon.
grated nutmeg
1 oz sultanas, optional

1 pt soya or almond milk
1 tblsp chopped dates
3 fl oz water
4 drops natural vanilla extract
or 1 vanilla pod

1   Place the chopped dates in the water and simmer until they are soft and mushy. Mix in the milk a little at a time beating the dates well so that they disintegrate sweetening the milk.

2   Place the milk, rice, cinnamon, sultanas and vanilla into a greased casserole dish. Sprinkle the surface liberally with grated nutmeg.

3   Bake at reg 6, 200c, 400f for approx 1 hr stirring occasionally. Remove the cinnamon stick before serving

ALMOND FRUIT BAKE (4)

3 oz ground almonds   *1 pt soya or almond milk*
2 tblsp rose water   *1 oz ground rice*
1 1/2 lb mixed fresh sweet fruit ie
cherries, apples, pears, peaches, apricots, plums.

1   Mix the ground rice with 2 fl oz cold milk. Bring the remaining
     milk to the boil, then mix in the ground rice stirring all the time
     until the mixture returns to the boil. Simmer stirring for 2 mins.
3   Add the ground almonds and rose water and stir well.
4   Pour into a shallow greased au gratin dish.
5   Remove the stones or cores from the fruit where necessary and
     slice the larger fruits. Arrange the fruit on top of the ground rice
     mixture in an attractive pattern, placing the cut sides
     downwards. Press the fruit well down.
6   Bake for approx 30 mins or until the fruit is cooked, at reg 6,
     200c, 400f. Serve hot or cold

Ground rice is not the same as rice flour. It is more coarsely ground.
In winter when a good selection of fresh fruit is not available try
serving with a mixture of fresh and stewed fruit ie. prune and pear
or apricot and apple.

STUFFED PEACHES (4)

4 lge peaches   *almond paste (see index)*
2 tblsp toasted slivered almonds

1   Make the almond paste as directed.
2   Half and stone the peaches and place in a baking dish, cut side uppermost (cut a little slice off the rounded edge if necessary to help them to remain stable).
3   Divide the almond paste into 8 pieces, roll into balls and place a ball in the centre of each peach half.
4   Bake covered for 10 mins, then uncovered for a further 10 mins at reg 6, 200c, 400f. The peaches should be soft and the filling just starting to brown.
5   Sprinkle with toasted slivered almonds before serving and serve either hot or cold.

FRIED BANANAS (4)

4 bananas   *1/2 tsp grated orange rind*
1 tsp sunflower oil   *1/2 tsp grated lemon rind*
1/2 tsp cinnamon   *juice 1 orange*
1 tblsp toasted slivered almonds

1   Peel the bananas and fry quickly in the oil until beginning to brown and soften on the outside. This will only take 2-3 mins.
2   Add the remaining ingredients, mix well and serve immediately.

Serve with vanilla custard, banana and mango ice cream, soya yogurt or just as they are. Using low salt butter to fry the bananas will give added flavour; if you are allowed dairy produce.

VANILLA CUSTARD (4)

2 tblsp fine maize meal
2 eggs, beaten
1/2 tsp natural vanilla
extract

1 pt soya or almond milk
2 tblsp finely chopped dates
2 fl oz water

1   Place the dates in the water in a saucepan and simmer until they are soft. Mix the maize meal and the milk and add to the dates a little at a time, beating well to enable the dates to disintegrate and sweeten the milk.
2   Add the eggs and vanilla extract.
3   Gradually bring the mixture to the boil stirring constantly, lower the heat and simmer for 1 min. Do not boil rapidly or the eggs will curdle.

If you cannot tolerate eggs use 4 level tblsp maize meal and make as above. A vanilla pod could be used instead of the vanilla extract.

SPONGE AND CUSTARD
Serve the custard with warm carrot and coconut cake, apple and date muffins or ginger and orange cake (see index)

PRUNES AND CUSTARD
Serve the custard with stewed prunes

BANANA CUSTARD
Cut 4 bananas into slices and add to the custard when it has cooled a little. Serve warm or allow to cool before serving.

BLACK FOREST TRIFLE
Crumble 1/3 of a carob birthday cake into a serving dish. Mix in two small tins of fruit in natural juice ie. strawberries, raspberries, blackberries. Pour over vanilla custard, allow to cool and serve.

BAKED EGG CUSTARD (4)

3 eggs, beaten
nutmeg

1 pt soya or almond milk
1/2 tsp natural vanilla extract

1 Grease an ovenproof dish and put in the beaten eggs.
2 Warm the milk in a saucepan until quite warm, then pour over the eggs, stirring thoroughly.
3 Add the vanilla extract and mix in. Then sprinkle the surface with nutmeg.
4 Place the dish in a baking tray which contains cold water. Then place the two dishes in the oven.
5 Bake at reg 3,170c, 325f for approx 30 mins or until the mixture is just setting in the centre. Do not overcook or the mixture will boil and curdle.

The custard will continue cooking for a little while once out of the oven. Serve with warm fruit compote, fried bananas or fresh fruit salad (see index). A vanilla pod could be used instead of the extract but will need soaking in the warm milk for 1/2 hr to allow the flavour to be absorbed. Remove the pod before baking.

FRUIT COMPOTE (4-6)

3/4 pt water
1 stick cinnamon or
1/2 tsp cinnamon

1 lb mixed dried fruit ie.
apricots, apples, prunes, figs
2 strips paired orange rind

1 Cut the orange rind into thin slivers and add to the water along with the fruit and cinnamon. Leave to soak overnight.
2 Bring to the boil and simmer for 15 mins until all the fruit is soft and the flavours have mingled.
3 Serve hot or cold.

The fruit can be cooked without soaking but it could take up to an hour to cook and more liquid will be needed as some will evaporate.

FRESH FRUIT SALAD (4-6)

1/4 carton fresh fruit juice ie. apple, orange, pineapple
1 1/2 lb fresh fruit selected from the following

apple	*banana*	*fresh dates*
grapes	*orange*	*blackberries*
pear	*melon*	*pineapple*
mango	*peach*	*passion fruit*
plums	*cherries*	*sharron fruit*
raspberries	*strawberries*	

1   Pour the fruit juice into a serving dish.
2   Peel, core and prepare the fruit and cut into even sized pieces.
3   Add to the fruit juice, mix well and chill before serving.

Use a little frozen fruit in winter to liven up a fresh fruit salad (ie. raspberries, blackberries) or an occasional tin of fruit in natural juice can be used as a base.

You do not have to use all the fruits available for a fruit salad. Try just serving 2-3 fruits ie.

melon and strawberry
orange and date
melon and black grape
pear, sharron fruit and raspberries.

A delicious desert can be made for entertaining by making a fruit salad of tropical fruits such as sharron fruit, dates, bananas, and mango and mixing with 3/4 pt of yogurt or preferably greek yogurt instead or the fruit juice. Add 1/2 cup of toasted flaked almonds and assemble just before serving to prevent the yogurt becoming watery and the nuts soft.

FRUIT TERRINE (4)

1/2 pt orange juice   *1/4 melon*
1 mango   *1/4 lb cherries*
1/4 lb grapes   *1/2 pkt (5 1/2 gm) gelatine or*
     the equivalent in gelozone

1   Peel and stone the fruit and dice the mango and melon. Layer the fruit in a terrine or loaf tin.
2   Warm the orange juice in a pan and sprinkle the gelatine onto the surface. Stir until dissolved.
3   Allow to cool a little then pour over the fruit in the terrine.
4   Refrigerate for a few hours until set, then serve cut into slices.

Gelozone is the vegetarian equivalent of gelatine, follow the directions for use from the packet. Other juices could be substituted for the orange juice but use juice from a carton rather then freshly squeezed as this is slightly less acidic. Other fruits can be substituted such as pear, peach, sharron fruit, banana, strawberries and fresh dates but do not use pineapple or paw paw as these will prevent the gelatine from setting.

FRUIT PLATTER

The same ingredients can be used but served on individual plates (preferably white). Arrange the fruit in an attractive pattern in the middle of each plate and pour the fruit juice and gelatine around the fruit. Allow to set as before.

JELLY

A plain jelly can be made for children by using 1 pt of fruit juice and a pkt of gelatine or gelozone. Warm the fruit juice and dissolve the gelatine in this. Place in a serving dish or mould and allow to cool in the fridge. Serve with fresh fruit, ice cream, yogurt or custard.

BANANA AND MANGO ICE CREAM

3 bananas   *1 lge mango*
5 fl oz soya or almond milk

1   Peel and slice the bananas and freeze in a container so that the
     bananas are not squashed together but will separate when
     frozen.
2   Peel and stone the mango and dice the flesh. Freeze in the same
     way as the banana.
3   Pour the milk into a food processor and switch onto full power. I
     wrap a tea towel round the processor to stop the milk
     splashing. Gradually add the banana and mango pieces through
     the funnel stopping if necessary to break the fruit up if it starts
     to stick together. Eventually you will obtain a smooth, creamy
     ice cream.
4   Serve at once or return to the freezer. If left in the freezer for
     long the ice cream will set quite hard and will then need to be
     left out to stand for approx 20 mins before serving

Serve the ice cream just as it is or along with other puddings. Vary
by adding toasted nuts or desiccated coconut. Finely chopped
crystallised ginger or candied peel can be added for those allowed a
little sugar, or for a desert when entertaining.

BANANA AND PEACH
Substitute 2 peaches for the mango in the above recipe.

STRAWBERRY AND BANANA
Substitute 10 oz strawberries for the mango in the above recipe.
Allow the strawberries to thaw for approx 5 mins before processing
as they are very solid when frozen.

STRAWBERRY AND PEACH SORBET
Freeze 10 oz strawberries and 2 peaches. Thaw for approx 5 mins
then process along with 4 fl oz fruit juice (orange, apple etc) or 4 fl
oz water

A wide range of ice creams and sorbets can be made using the above
method but substituting different fruits. Yogurt can be used instead
of the milk for another variation.

SWEET SOUFFLE OMELETTE (2)

2 eggs   2 tblsp water
1 tsp sunflower oil   1 dsp marmalade or
                                     mincemeat (see index)

1   Separate the yolks from the whites putting them in separate
    bowls. Add the water to the yolks and mix well.
2   Whisk the egg whites until stiff and fold gently into the egg
    yolks with a metal spoon.
3   Cook in an omelette pan in the oil over a medium heat until the
    underside of the omelette is golden brown.
4   Place the pan under the grill until the omelette is brown on top
    and set.
5   Spread the marmalade or mincemeat over the omelette and fold
    in half. Serve at once.

STUFFED PANCAKES (4)

1 egg   8 fl oz water or a mixture
4 oz rice flour   of water and soya milk
1/2 tsp cinnamon   1 tsp potassium B.P.
1/4 tsp lemon rind   1 dsp sunflower oil

1   Blend all the ingredients except the oil in the food processor. If
    mixing by hand beat the eggs then add the remaining
    ingredients except the oil and beat well.
2   Oil a pan or griddle and cook 4 pancakes. Turn the pancakes as
    soon as they are puffed and full of bubbles .

BANANA PANCAKES
Roll each pancake round a small peeled banana. Heat through and
serve with soya yogurt, ice cream, carob cream or vanilla custard.

MINCEMEAT OR MARMALADE PANCAKES
Spread each pancake with mincemeat or marmalade (see index),
fold into quarters and serve with vanilla custard or soya yogurt.

FRUIT PANCAKES
Serve with stewed dried fruit or fresh fruit and vanilla custard, etc.

MELON WITH MANGO SAUCE (4)

1 small or 1/2 lge melon   *3 passion fruit*
1 lge or 2 small mangos

1   Cube or ball the melon flesh. Peel the mango and slice the flesh
     from the stone.
2   Liquidize the mango, the flesh from the passion fruit and a
     quarter of the melon to make a smooth sauce. If you have used a
     melon baller for the melon, liquidize the leftover pieces of melon.
3   Sieve the sauce to remove the passion fruit seeds. Serve the
     melon in sundae glasses with the sauce poured over.

SPICED PEARS (4)

3 lge firm pears   *1/2 tsp ground cardamom*
4 fl oz apple juice   *1/2 tsp cinnamon*
                                 1/4 tsp ground cloves

1   Peel and quarter the pears and cut away the cores.
2   Cut the pears into 1/2" lengthwise slices and place in an
     ovenproof dish.
3   Sprinkle with the spices and pour the apple juice over.
4   Cover and bake at reg 6, 200c, 400f for approx 20 mins or until
     tender.

Serve hot or cold just as they are or with vanilla custard, soya yogurt
or ice cream.

CHRISTMAS PUDDING
Makes 3 puddings to serve 4 people

1 portion of Christmas cake recipe (see index)
2 lge grated carrots
8 oz baking apples, peeled and grated.
2 heaped tsps potassium B.P.

1   Mix the cake ingredients as per recipe (I double the quantity and make both puddings and cake on the same day to save time.)
2   Mix in the grated carrots, apple and baking powder.
3   Divide the mixture into greased pudding basins depending on the size of the puddings you require.
4   Steam, pressure cook or microwave the puddings according to their size. The 4 person pudding will take 30 mins in the pressure cooker, 2 hrs over boiling water and 12 mins in the microwave on power level 5.

I freeze any puddings which will not be used within one week as they will not keep for too long.
Serve with vanilla custard.

STUFFED DATES OR PRUNES.

24 moist stoned prunes, pitted dates or fresh dates
1/2 cup nut butter (almond, cashew or hazelnut)
24 walnut halves

1   With a sharp knife, slice open each date or prune lengthwise along one side.
2   Fill each with 1/2 tsp nut butter, then press a nut into the centre.

These will keep well in the fridge for a few weeks and are ideal to have in at Christmas time or when entertaining.

WHY YOU SHOULD AVOID WHEAT, DAIRY PRODUCE, SATURATED FAT, SALT, SUGAR AND YEAST.

WHEAT

Wheat as a dietary constituent has some advantages but on the whole these are outweighed by its disadvantages. Wheat is generally thought of as a wholesome, nutritious, fibre rich food, but unfortunately for many individuals (including many who don't realise), wheat is actually causing them problems.

Wheat contains gluten which when wet is a sticky glue-like substance. It isn't long ago that flour and water were used as a cheap glue. In our gut this glue can play havoc with the digestion and absorption of nutrients. Because gluten is so sticky and difficult to digest it encourages the growth of unfriendly bacteria (see candida) which are responsible for producing toxic substances and gas. Constipation, diarrhoea, bloatedness, indigestion, flatulence or wind are all problems which will benefit from the removal of wheat from the diet.

Of the foods which people become allergic to, wheat is one of the most common. Wheat can make an individual feel tired, irritable and depressed as well as aggravating other diseases, such as arthritis, psoriasis and eczema. Because most people eat wheat so often, the body adapts and copes and they are unaware that it does not agree with them (see allergies). However, once it is removed from the diet many individuals notice tremendous improvements in their health and well being.

Wheat has a suppressive action on the liver so even individuals who seem to tolerate wheat well, slow down their rate of elimination by eating wheat too often. Wheat is therefore best avoided in the early stages of elimination and especially if your health is seriously below par. After working on the eating regime outlined in this book to a point where you feel fit and healthy, try including wheat again, but never include it in large quantities and never more than once per day. Other grains which contain gluten are rye, oats and barley, and although some individuals may tolerate these better than wheat others may need to avoid them completely until their health has improved.

MILK

Milk has an image of being the perfect food but it is only the perfect food when fed from the mother to her infant. Eventually a young child loses the enzyme necessary to digest milk and after this stage milk becomes acid and mucous forming, capable of upsetting normal bowel flora and preventing the absorption of vitamins and minerals. Many individuals develop allergies to milk and its products which they are not aware of until milk is removed from the diet.

In general we are led to believe that we don't obtain sufficient calcium and that milk and milk products are essential. However if there is a problem with inadequate calcium it is far more likely to be through poor absorption than through poor intake. Calcium is readily available in foods such as vegetables, fruit, nuts and pulses.

If our diet and absorption are improved we can live more healthily without milk. This can be seen in many tribal communities where milk and milk products are not consumed yet children grow well, producing good bones and teeth and diseases such as arthritis and osteoporosis are unknown

CHEESE

Cheese not only has the negative aspects of milk but it is also high in fat and salt and is difficult to digest. Cottage cheese is more acceptable once health has been obtained.

BUTTER

Butter is the fatty part of the milk but because little of the milk remains it can often be tolerated by those allergic to milk. If a form of fat is used for spreading I think that butter is preferable to the chemically derived margarines, but it should be used in moderation.

YOGURT

Live yogurt is the most favourable of all milk products due to the fact that it is low in fat and is partly digested by the action of the micro-organisms. These micro-organisms assist in the repopulation of the intestinal tract with friendly bacteria.Yogurt does however still carry the negative aspects of milk and is often better tolerated if made from sheep or goats milk.

FATS AND OILS

Fats and oils can be categorised into polyunsaturates, monounsaturates and saturates.

Saturated fats are the ones we are constantly being told to cut down on and all the recipes in this book are free from saturated fat. However I feel that the reason our bodies do not cope well nowadays with saturated fat is because we are so toxic and lacking in vitamins and minerals. The liver which is our main organ of detoxification is also the main organ which deals with fat. If the liver is struggling to detoxify it will also be struggling to cope with fat.

The liver is also the organ which balances the production of cholesterol in the body. Cholesterol is a fat which has gained a bad reputation as far as health is concerned, its excess being associated with such as heart attacks and strokes. But cholesterol is needed by the body for many different bodily functions and if we do not absorb sufficient from our food, the liver is capable of making more. Equally if we have too much cholesterol, the liver is capable of removing any excess by excreting it in the form of bile acids. However in order to perform this cholesterol balancing act efficiently the liver is dependent on an adequate supply of nutriments and energy being obtained from the diet. Cooking Without aims to supply these.

Excess cholesterol which is excreted from the body via the bile is accompanied by any toxicity which the body needs to remove. It is therefore important that we encourage a good bile flow and in order to do this we do need some fat in the diet as bile is released in response to fat or oil being digested. Therefore do not completely remove fat or oil from your diet.

For the toxicity and excess cholesterol to be excreted from the body once they are in the digestive tract adequate amounts of fibre are needed to assist their elimination. This prevents them from being re-absorbed back into the body.

The diet outlined in this book enables an adequate intake of fat and plenty of fibre to be consumed. As far as I am concerned the reason why our ancestors could eat a high fat diet and not have the trouble with such as heart attacks is that they had the necessary vitamins, minerals and fibre in their diets, and they were not overloaded with toxicity.

It is best to limit saturated fats whilst detoxifying but don't be obsessive about removing every scrap. Individuals are often told not to eat eggs because they are high in fat and cholesterol but eggs also contain lecithin a fat emulsifier and are quite acceptable used in sensible quantities. Even meat which is lean does contain saturated fat and so it is sensible to eat a varied diet which contains some fish and a number of vegetarian days. Although coconut is of vegetable origin it does contain the most saturated vegetable oil and so it should be used sparingly. Butter I feel is the most acceptable substance for spreading and is quite admissible if used in small quantities.

Monounsaturated fats include olive oil and although little has been spoken of monounsaturates in the past they are now being regarded as helpful fats in the diet (the mediterranean diet contains olive oil). Olive oil is also the most stable oil when heated. However all oils when heated become increasingly toxic so limit very hot frying. Do include some monounsaturated oil in your diet, either in the form of foods (ie olives), in salad dressings or as a teaspoonful poured over rice or vegetables.

Polyunsaturated oils are the ones we have been constantly encouraged to use but this is not necessarily a good idea. All oils contain essential fatty acids but linolenic acid is the essential fatty acid which we are most in need of. This is obtained best from eating fish (preferably oily), green leafy vegetables or from linseed oil and linseeds.

Unfortunately if we eat too many polyunsaturates, linolenic acid (the one we most need) is outweighed by linoleic acid which these polyunsaturated oils contain and this causes an imbalance in our bodies. Therefore polyunsaturated oils are best used in moderation with fish, green vegetables and linseed oil being consumed to provide a balance. Most margarines are made from polyunsaturates but they are also produced using chemicals and are then partly hydrogenated which turns some of the polyunsaturates into saturated fat. The hydrogenation process also causes the production of free radicals (harmful substances) and changes the structure of the oil from a "cis" form to a "trans" form. This "trans" form is rarely found in nature and is therefore unacceptable to the human body. Avoid the use of margarine unless you cannot tolerate butter in which case find one of the margarines which is not hydrogenated and is high in "cis" form fatty acids.

Certain measures can be taken to safeguard the use of fats and oils in the diet.

1   Consume most oils in the form of foods ie. nuts, seeds, olives, beans ,sweetcorn, and linseeds.
2   Include some linseed oil in your daily diet to balance linolenic acid with linoleic acid. Linseeds can be bought from health food shops and are pleasant to take, sprinkled on breakfast cereals, salads, soups etc. Try taking 1-2 dsp per day for a real health benefit. Linseed oil can be taken from the spoon or used in salad dressings and on vegetables. 1-2 tsps per day would be helpful.
3   Use cold pressed oils, heavily processed oils will have suffered oxidative and chemical damage.
4   Buy oils in small glass bottles and store in the fridge.
5   Improving nutrition will enable fats in any form to be more readily assimilated by the body.

SALT

Sodium is an essential mineral in the body and together with potassium, magnesium and calcium it forms one of the four bulk minerals. An over consumption of salt upsets the delicate balance between these minerals, and the accumulation of sodium in the cells causes the latter to become more acidic. Other micro minerals such as zinc and selenium which the body may be deficient in will not be readily absorbed unless the four bulk minerals are well balanced in our bodies.

Our bodies do need some salt as sodium is lost through the skin and faeces. Approx half a gram per day is needed and this small amount can easily be obtained by eating natural foods such as vegetables.

Salt is not the only form of sodium to enter into our bodies. Others forms include monosodium glutamate (used as a flavour enhancer), sodium bicarbonate (used in baking powder), sodium nitrate and nitrite (used as preservatives), and hydrolysed proteins (used in stock cubes).

Avoid adding salt to your food for at least three months. You will then start to taste the food rather than the salt and you will find many of the previous things you ate as being too salty. If salt is then needed in the occasional soup or casserole you will have the ability to add it in order to improve the taste. You should not need to put salt in cooked vegetables, grains etc or on the table.

Seaweed although salty is full of minerals and I feel it is acceptable in the small quantities that would be consumed.

SUGAR

If we ate sugar in its natural form of fruit or sugar cane there would be a limit to how much sugar we could consume. Along with the sugar, we would obtain lots of fibre and the vitamins and minerals needed to digest the sugar. The fibre content means that it would take time to break down the structure and release the sugar into the bloodstream.

If however we eat manufactured sugar or products made from this (biscuits, cakes, sweets etc) then we encourage low blood sugar or hypoglycaemia. This sudden surge of sugar into the bloodstream and its removal by the pancreas results in the roller coaster effects of cravings, highs and then lows which leave us feeling physically, mentally and emotionally below par. (see "how blood sugar works") Sugar encourages the overgrowth of bad intestinal flora and should be avoided in all its forms. Brown sugar although retaining some nutrients still contains 97% white sugar.

When health has been obtained a little honey, molasses or no sugar fruit spread is acceptable.

YEAST AND FERMENTED PRODUCTS

Because yeast related products can aggravate candida symptoms and upset the digestive tract it is best to avoid these products on a temporary basis and then watch how your body reacts as you re-introduce them at a later date. They include yeast, yeast extract, vinegar, citric acid, monosodium glutamate, stock cubes, tofu, miso, tamari and shoyu sauce, alcohol, cheese, mushrooms and dried fruit.

I find that mushrooms and tofu if used in small quantities are quite acceptable for many candida sufferers. Dried fruit can also be used sparingly for many candida sufferers provided it is washed well to remove the yeasts which are on the surface. Miso, tamari and shoyu sauce are the most acceptable flavourings to use in cooking but individuals will need to test these to see how they react.

TEA AND COFFEE

Most people use tea and coffee to give them a lift. They do this because these beverages contain drug-like substances which kick the body and cause a release of blood sugar. This means that one is not working on natural energy but is flogging an otherwise "dead horse".

Try alternatives but realise that it may take time for you to acquire a taste for them. Also accept that you will miss tea and coffee - remember they are drugs. Persevere and make the change over gradually.

ADDITIVES

These include such things as colourings, flavourings, preservatives, antioxidants, emulsifiers, stabilisers, sweeteners and modified starches.
Additives are mostly chemically derived and as such are another toxic substance for the body to deal with. Additives such as flavourings will often contain a hundred different chemicals just to produce one flavour. They have been shown to cause epileptic fits, asthma and hyperactivity but often the underlying damage they are causing is not seen. Learn to read labels before you buy, but do be aware that some additives are naturally derived and are acceptable.

SOME COMMON HEALTH PROBLEMS

CANDIDA ALBICANS

Inside our intestinal tract are minute organisms called intestinal flora which are bacteria responsible in part for the absorption of nutrients and the elimination of waste products. Among these bacteria both good and bad exist but normally the bad bacteria don't cause us any problems provided we have sufficient natural defenses, or good bacteria to keep them in their place. Nowadays one particular bad bacteria called Candida is being encouraged to get out of hand and its overgrowth is causing the individuals concerned a lot of problems. This overgrowth is being caused by the way we eat, chlorine in our water supplies and the widespread use of the pill, antibiotics and hormones (either taken as medication or in our meat)

Once out of hand the Candida eventually punctures the gut wall. The wall which is normally very particular about what it allows through is now open to absorb larger particles such as food which has not been completely digested, toxicity from the gut and Candida itself. The immune system recognises these particles as foreign and should produce antibodies to protect us against further invasion. If however the immune system is overburdened with toxicity and lacking in essential nutrients then the immune system is weakened and is unable to defend itself. Candida is allowed to spread unhampered into the body and an immune response or allergy is set up. Both allergies and low blood sugar are frequent forerunners of Candida.

Here is a list of some of the symptoms which can be attributed to Candida's overgrowth :- cystitis, thrush, fungal infections, PMT, endometriosis, abdominal bloating, indigestion, flatulence, diarrhoea, constipation, bad breath, acne, numbness, tingling, recurrent sore throats, blurred vision, lethargy, mood swings, anxiety, depression, muscle aches, itching, headaches, muzziness, dizziness, lack of concentration, memory lapses and many more.

As can be seen from the above list Candida Albicans merits attention, but all too frequently the attention is directed obsessively at killing the Candida without reference to the individuals body which has allowed the invasion to take place. Candida is present in all of us and can never be completely eliminated and therefore working in isolation on trying to kill or starve the Candida means that as soon as treatment stops it will thrive again.

Candida grows in an acidic environment within the intestinal tract. The environment in the cells of a healthy body whose mineral status is good is slightly alkaline. Therefore even if Candida reached these cells, in a healthy person its growth would be discouraged and it would die. However what is happening nowadays is that our cells are becoming more acidic and our bodies and immune systems are unable to protect themselves against Candida invasion. Increased levels of acidity in the cells are being caused by the widespread consumption of acid forming foods (meat, tea, coffee, alcohol etc) and a lack of alkaline forming foods (mainly fruit and vegetables) together with the fact that a lot of the food we do eat is lacking in minerals, over processed and laden with chemical additives.

The only real answer to Candida problems is to detoxify the body and replenish its mineral reserves. By working on the dietary regime outlined in this book the cells will gradually lose their acidity and will become slightly alkaline, the immune system will be strengthened and the Candida will no longer be able to take over.

Too many Candida diets cause individuals to starve themselves by excessively limiting foods. For instance many Candida regimes remove carbohydrates completely. This is based on the theory that carbohydrates convert to sugar and sugar feeds Candida. However limiting carbohydrates encourages toxic symptoms as toxicity is released from the cells in response to fasting (hardly eating) or a diet which is high in vegetables and low in carbohydrates.

In order for this toxicity to be removed from the body, the body needs energy (blood sugar) to work the elimination system. It also needs a medium which will soak up the acid waste or toxicity and remove it from the body. Complex carbohydrates are the only foods which fulfil these two roles. What is frequently termed "die-off" in many Candida books and is supposedly caused by Candida dying and releasing its toxicity, is as far as I am concerned a build up of toxicity caused by eating insufficient of the right kinds of foods. It happens with all patients who limit the quantity of food they eat, especially carbohydrates, whether they suffer from Candida symptoms or other problems.

The regime outlined in this book is ideal for Candida sufferers even though it is high in carbohydrates. These carbohydrates are complex in form and will be tolerated by all except a very small minority who have allergies to certain foods. Care may be needed with fresh fruit and dried fruit should be avoided initially and washed well to remove yeasts when introduced. Yeast and fermented products as well as cereals containing gluten are best avoided and mushrooms may need to be avoided in the early stages.

On an emotional level Candida sufferers are lacking in self worth and are very hard on themselves (see section"Emotions, addictions and ill health"). Even if they do not try to be Superman or Superwoman, they still push and expect too much of their bodies. The reasons that cause Candida sufferers to be so hard on themselves will be uncovered as detoxification takes place. These reasons which can be termed emotional toxicity will be eliminated along with the physical toxicity present in the body.

ALLERGIES AND INTOLERANCES

Nowadays allergies are very common and many individuals spend a lot of time and money being tested to find the substances which are causing them problems. However just avoiding these substances is not the permanent answer to allergies. It is important to realise that unless one finds the root of the allergy problem (that is why the individual has become allergic in the first place) the body will persist in producing more allergies and its health will continue to deteriorate.

The immune system is a complex army of cells and antibodies which protect the body from external invaders. When working harmoniously the immune system protects us from many micro-organisms some of which cause infectious diseases. However when the cells of the body and immune system are overburdened with toxicity there is a tendency for the immune system to over react to invaders. This causes the production of allergy symptoms. It can also cause a drop in blood sugar levels because of the stress the allergy creates. Mineral and vitamin deficiencies go hand in hand with excess toxicity and so aggravate the problem. Candida is often responsible for the immune system being invaded. As well as Candida, partly digested food and toxicity from the gut reach the immune system once the gut wall has been punctured.

Many individuals are being affected by allergies which can be termed "hidden", or "masked" allergies. This means that they do not produce symptoms which are typically linked to allergies such as spots or rashes but these masked allergies are undermining health in a more subtle way. The foods or substances which cause masked allergies tend to be the ones we come into contact with on a fairly regular basis such as bread or milk. In these cases individuals can get hooked on the food causing problems and so crave and temporarily feel better for eating this food. However once it is removed from the diet many individuals notice tremendous improvements in their health and state of well being.

It is obviously useful in the short term to remove the main foods likely to cause allergy problems, but in order to obtain long term benefits toxicity must be removed from the cells of the immune system and the vitamin and mineral depletion in the cells must be rectified. The intestinal wall must be allowed to rebuild itself by improving the levels of good intestinal flora in the gut.

If having followed the regime outlined in this book for a few months you are still having problems then an allergy test may be necessary. It is always possible that you are reacting to one of the foods that you are still eating.

Eventually foods which caused problems can be re-introduced but this should be done gradually once health has been regained. If you introduce them too soon you may find that you re-act to them more strongly than you did before. This is because having removed them from the body it has lost its ability to adapt or cope. Don't worry about this and continue working on improving your health and eventually they will be accepted. Never introduce more than one food at a time and don't overeat new foods even if you can tolerate them.

M.E. (MYALGIC ENCEPHALOMYELITIS) and
T.T.T. (TIRED ALL THE TIME)

ME is not always what it seems to be. Those who accept it exists are usually looking to blame a virus. However the virus is really irrelevant, as many people with ME symptoms do not have a virus present and many with the virus present are fit and healthy. Many individuals with ME are sick because their immune systems have been weakened allowing them to be prey to any virus which comes along. It is no use trying to find the magic bullet which will kill the virus but rather a matter of looking at why the immune system has been compromised and working at strengthening it.Candida weakens the body and the immune system and many ME sufferers have Candida present. The body and immune system can also be weakened by stress, by poor nutrition and by general toxicity whether it be from a toxic laden diet, drug abuse or environmental pollution. Antibiotic over-use and vaccinations are frequent forerunners of ME symptoms.

ME has been referred to as "yuppie flu" and it is no coincidence that these ambitious over achievers are susceptible to the problem. Like most ME sufferers they have been living on adrenalin and pushing their bodies for too long. They may get up feeling tired but once into the swing of the day the adrenalin starts to flow and they feel fine. Later when the energy flags a game of squash or a three mile jog gives their adrenals another kick and they are ready for a busy evening. Add to this the type of lifestyle that many young people live, eating too much junk food, missing meals, partaking of alcohol, taking the pill, taking antibiotics for infections and you can see how eventually the body must give in. The mother who works or the overstressed business man may not have the glamorous lifestyle of the yuppie but the effects of living on the adrenalin are the same. ME is not a disease but a series of symptoms which the body is using as a signal to let the individual know that all is not well. Infact everything is exhausted.

ME can be seen at one end of the scale in individuals who generally do not feel well, but cope each day with a multitude of minor health problems and a continual lack of energy. They struggle by living on the adrenalin and pushing their bodies to keep going. These individuals are on the verge of ME and it only takes a strong antibiotic from the doctor, a dose of flu or a severely stressful situation to push them over the edge. At the other end of the scale are those ME sufferers who are so sick and weak they can barely stand up. They may ache from head to toe, find it impossible to think or concentrate, feel permanently sick or dizzy ,and will have many more individual symptoms.

In order to recover from ME work needs to be done on raising the blood sugar levels. This relieves some of the symptoms which are due to low blood sugar (see "how blood sugar works") and takes pressure off the adrenal glands which are exhausted. The dietary regime outlined in this book is ideal for this. ME is similar to Candida in that it cannot be treated as an isolated problem without the individual who developed ME being taken into consideration. Work needs to be done on detoxifying the body and replacing lost minerals in an attempt to repair and support all the organs, glands and systems which have become implicated. The issue of self worth needs consideration because a lack of self worth is frequently the motivator for over achievement. (see "Emotions, addictions and ill health")

EMOTIONS, ADDICTIONS AND ILL HEALTH.

Addictions are very common in our society and range from the more acceptable ones such as sugar or chocolate addictions to the more severe drug and alcohol based ones. In between is a range which includes, spending, smoking, gambling, men, women, sex, shoplifting and any more you can think of.

What each of these addictions does is to temporarily make us feel better. The fact that the consequences might be injurious to us is irrelevant at the time; we know that we will feel better if we have a chocolate bar, find a new lover, buy ourselves a new stereo, or have a drink, but what we are actually doing is avoiding facing the reality of our situation. When we come down from the high that addictions create often we feel worse than before. Unless individuals find the reasons why they are addicted they will not recover or they will swap one addiction for another.

Within each of us is a male and female side of our personality, the animus and anima (see chart). The animus or male psyche used positively is responsible for drive, ambition, determination, self reliance and discipline. The female anima used positively is responsible for feelings, emotions, intuition, softness and caring.

We are all born with different personalities, some females have a strong animus or male side and would not be happy staying at home.They want to be out there in the world of work. Similarly some men who have a strong anima to contend with are not assertive enough to work in the world of business but are happy in the caring professions or at home with the children.What is important is that we learn to be true to ourselves and find our own balance between the anima and animus. If however we have been brought up to suppress one side of our personality or overemphasise the other, then often illness or addictive behaviour takes over.

This affects mostly those individuals who have an innately strong feminine side which they have learnt to repress or hide. Those with an innately strong masculine side will fit more easily into the roles which parents and society deem acceptable.

THE ANIMUS ANIMA CHART

ANIMA (female psyche)

POSITIVE ASPECTS

Being aware of needs
Learning to give to self
Learning to accept self
Learning to love self
Learning to say "no".

NEGATIVE ASPECTS

Illness
Addictions ie.
    smoking
    alcohol
    food
    men/women
    spending
    gambling

Replace negative animus with positive anima

Enables one to use the positive animus

And not need the negative anima

ANIMUS (male psyche)

NEGATIVE ASPECTS

Being a workaholic
Compulsive or
Obsessive behaviour
Perfectionism
Self denial
Feeling a failure

POSITIVE ASPECTS

Working well
Being organised
Confidence
Self reliance
Self discipline
Stability
Independence
Accomplishment

Childhood upbringing has a lot to do with the way we are. Often parents have taught individuals not to be selfish or acknowledge their own needs (religions may have encouraged this). This lack of self acknowledgement may have been passed on by parents who themselves had problems. Perhaps they couldn't express their emotions and in doing so inadvertently taught the child to hide its feelings, or perhaps the child received very little attention so that it only felt acknowledged when it did something exceptional. Thus it always had to drive itself hard and aim continually higher in order to gain a reward. Whatever the background, and this can be as varied as the individuals with the problems, what is unfortunately being taught is a lack of self worth.The feminine side which enables one to love, cherish and be kind to oneself is suppressed and the masculine side is encouraged, becomes overdeveloped and expresses itself negatively. Thus instead of working well, individuals become workaholics, instead of being self disciplined they become self denying, instead of being organised they become perfectionists. Each person finds their own way of validating their self worth dependent on their individual talents. Others will turn this drive inwards and will just be hard on themselves ie. "I'm a failure" or "I'm useless".

In the middle of the chart is a pendulum which will always find a persons true balance between their masculine and feminine. If the pendulum has swung too far to the left because an individual has been working too hard or expecting too much of themselves then it will need to swing excessively to the right to rebalance. If they are able to compensate by being kind and giving to themselves then all will be well, but what happens if they have run out of time or have never been taught to love and nurture themselves?

Addictions and illness become an alternative that satisfies a deep yearning within the subconscious, and so after a hard day individuals may turn to such as food, alcohol or sex in order to try to rebalance. Similarly being ill means that they are forced to give themselves time and attention or allow others to do this by nursing them better. The feminine side may be lived out through illness or addictions but unless it is owned by oneself then peace, health or happiness will never be fully attained.

In order to rebalance the feminine and masculine it is first of all necessary for individuals to see how these two are being used in their lives. Being aware of when and how they are using the negative animus is the first step. A good way of thinking of this, is like a shadow self walking behind one with a whip, always pushing and tormenting and expecting more. All individuals who are ill or have addictions have far higher expectations of themselves than they do of anyone else. Once one realises how and when the whip is being used it is much easier not to expect oneself to be superman or superwoman.

Rebuilding the positive side of the anima is about learning to be kind to oneself, to give and to indulge. It is the process of learning to understand ones needs, to love, nurture and accept oneself despite any imperfections and is the basis of developing real self worth.

A good idea is to write a list of twenty positive ways to "give to oneself." Often individuals are indulging with sweets, alcohol, spending etc but then feeling really bad and being hard on themselves for doing so (the animus again). These new ways are all about invoking feelings of "this is nice," "this is for me," "I deserve this,". The list will vary from person to person, for what makes one of us feel guilty and indulgent will not do the same for another. It is not the issue that's important, it's the feelings of love we invoke when we do these things that we are trying to foster. The list can include things as simple as :- a pot of tea with time to sit and savour it; a lazy bath; an early night; reading; walking; looking at the view; watching the cat; buying oneself a bunch of flowers.

Some individuals may say, "Oh, that's not me, I always buy myself presents, have an early night etc, but often they are doing these things for the wrong reasons. Are they buying new clothes because they deserve them or because their self worth is invested in looking good? Are they indulging in an early night because they feel they would like it or to escape from reality?

By learning to be kind to ourselves we gradually discover that we have needs and that these needs must be met if we are to stay healthy. We also learn to love ourselves sufficiently to put satisfying these needs as a priority in our life and learn sufficient self worth to be able to say "No" when others try to distract us. An example of this might be someone who needs their own space but has a partner and family who are clingy and always demanding attention. Rather than feeling like a bad person who must be a failure and must work harder at their marriage and relationships this person needs to accept that this is the way they are, that freedom is one of their needs and must be satisfied.

Although this all seems very indulgent and selfish so is being ill or addicted. It is far better to give oneself the time, attention and love now whilst one is still able, rather than keep denying oneself now and eventually needing to be looked after. Because the male animus is overdeveloped it is easy to turn indulgences into animus things. For instance, we may say to ourselves,"I'm going to read my book tonight", but instead of doing it with love we do it with the whip, "You will find time to read that book". Suddenly it has changed from a feminine, caring action into a driving ambition. In this instance it is better to swap what we intended doing for something else."Instead of the book which I'm too tired to read I'm going to have an early night."

Eventually we can stop the pendulum swinging so wildly and decrease our need for addictions and illness by learning to live out the positive sides of the anima and animus. Following the diet outlined in Cooking Without will assist in this process. Because Cooking Without is designed to detoxify it will help you to work through mental and emotional toxicity which may have caused you to use the negative expressions of the anima and animus. Individuals who have worked on themselves in this way are then able to tap into the feminine qualities of feeling and intuition to see their path in life more clearly. The new base of confidence and self reliance which they have created by utilizing the very positive attributes of the animus will enable them to move forward along this path more easily.

USEFUL ADDRESSES

SPNT (Society for the Promotion of Nutritional Therapy)
PO Box 47, Heathfield. East Sussex. TN21 8ZX. Tel 01435 867007.
An educational and campaigning organisation with lay and practitioner members. Send SAE and £1 for information and a list of your nearest qualified nutritional therapists.

ION (The Institute of Optimum Nutrition)
Blades Court, Deodar Rd. London. SW15 2NU. Tel 0181 877 9993
ION exists as an independent charity to help you achieve optimum health. ION offers short courses, homestudy courses, books ,a magazine, consultations and a Nutrition Consultants diploma course.

CYTOPLAN LTD.
205 West Malvern Rd. West Malvern. Worcs. WR14 4BB. Tel 01684 577777. Stockists of food state supplements. Nutritional advise line on 01684 576742.

HIGHER NATURE LTD.
Burwash Common, East Sussex. TN19 7LX. Tel 01435 882880.
Catologue of nutritional supplements and free magazine available on request. Also a nutrition helpline for your queries or nutrition consultations by phone or in person.

YORK NUTRITIONAL LABORATORY.
Tudor House. Lysander Close. Clifton Moor. York. YO3 4XB. Tel 01904 690640. Offers cytotoxic blood tests for allergies and intolerances.

ALLERGY CARE (Foodwatch)
Pollards Yard. Wood St. Taunton. Somerset. TA1 1UP. Tel 01823 325023. Mail order suppliers of alternative and substitute food products. Also a team of qualified allergy testers (using vega testing) working in over 500 centres throughout the UK.

CHARLES GORDON.
Gordon House, Little Mead Industrial Estate. Cranleigh. Surrey.
GU6 8ND. Suppliers of mustard flour with no other added ingredients and English mustard with salt, water and spices added.

170

INDEX

BREAKFASTS

Almond milk	31	Potato cakes	34
Apricot spread	32	Potato pancakes	36
Banana and maize cereal	30	Rice porridge	28
Breakfast in a glass	32	Rice with leeks and	
Breakfast rice	29	scrambled eggs	34
Bubble and squeak	36	Sago breakfast cereal	30
Egg fried rice	33	Scrambled tofu with	
Light muesli	27	sweetcorn and arame	33
Marmalade	32	Soaked muesli	28
Millet porridge	27	Soya milk yogurt	31
Muesli	27	Sweetcorn + onion fritters	35
Pear and carob cereal	29	Trad English breakfast	35

STARTERS

Asparagus with leeks		Country salad	43
and walnut mayonnaise	44	Hors d'oeuvres with	
Avocado + cashew nut pate	40	garlic mayonnaise	44
Avocado dip	40	Humous and crudities	42
Avocado and mango	42	Savoury fruit salad	43
Avocado and tomato	42	Spinach + carrot timbale	39
Butterbean, mint and		Stuffed lettuce leaves	38
tuna pate	41	Warm chicken liver	
Carrot and apricot pate	40	salad	39
Carrot and cashew pate	41		

SOUPS

Butterbean and vegetable	50	Gazpacho	52
Carrot and cardamon	49	Leekie millet broth	48
Carrot and coriander	49	Leek, sweetcorn + almond	53
Carrot and tomato	49	Light lentil	47
Cauliflower and cashew	52	Majorcan soup	53
Chicken and seaweed	54	Parsnip and onion	51
Fennel, celery and leek	48	Pea soup	47
Fish soup	51	Quick vegetable + lentil	50

SALADS

All in one salad	59	Curried egg + rice	64
Apple, carrrot + ginger	58	Hazelnut + rice	58
Apple, celery + beetroot	56	Jellied beetroot	61
Avocado + grapefruit	56	Jellied carrot	61
Avocado, sweetcorn + olive	58	Leaf green, arame	
Avocado, tofu + pineapple	56	and satsuma	58
Bean + sweetcorn	56	Mediterranean lentil	62
Bean + pepper	56	Millet tabouli	62
Beansprout + cauliflower	56	Minted avocado + chickpea	60
Beansprout + sweetcorn	56	Pineapple and olive	58
Beetroot + pineapple	56	Red cabbage	63
Broccoli + red bean	58	Rice and carrot	58
Carrot + beetroot	56	Rice pilaff ring	63
Chicken, egg, almond		Rice, sweetcorn + beans	58
and potato	61	Root veg and raisin	56
Coleslaw	59	Tomato + coriander	58
Cucumber, mint + yogurt	58	Tropical curried chicken	64
Courgette + cauliflower	56	Tuna + bean	56
Curried apple coleslaw	60	Tuna + celery	61

MAINLY VEGETARIAN

Bean + vegetable casserole	85	Rice with sweetcorn and	
Biriani with rice	93	coconut	91
Black eyed bean and		Seafood lasagne	82
vegetable terrine	72	Savoury pancakes	71
Brazilian stir fry	77	Squirrel's delight	73
Broccoli + smoked tofu		Stir fried vegetables	
bake	86	with toasted cashews	76
Broccoli + sweetcorn		Stuffed aubergines	90
quiche	78	Stuffed baked potatoes	83
Carrot + coconut rice	91	Stuffed marrow	90
Carrot + courgette bake	68	Stuffed peppers	84
Carrot + leek quiche	79	Sushi	91
Cauliflower + courgette		Vegetable and cashew	
bake	70	nut medley	87
Lentil bolognese	67	Vegetable + fruit kebabs	75
Lentil bolognese pancakes	71	Veg + fruit rogan josh	94

Lentil lasagne	82	Vegetable chilli with	
Lentil moussaka	67	walnuts and quinoa	66
Millet + walnut bake	69	Vegetable crumble	86
Mushroom curry	93	Vegetable lasagne	82
Nut roast	74	Vegetable masala	92
Nutty vegetable loaf	72	Veg masala pancakes	71
Polenta pizza	81	Vegetable risotto	76
Potato, courgette and		Vegetable rogan josh	94
aubergine bake	80	Vegetarian shepherds pie	68
Potato + parsnip pie	88	Winter bean + tofu	
Quick bean curry	93	casserole	84
Ratatouille pancakes	71		

MEAT DISHES

Chicken casserole	97	Lamb with nut pilau	104
Chicken curry	96	Lamb with orange	
Chicken brazilian	97	and ginger	102
Chicken liver risotto	100	Rabbit or chicken with	
Chicken polo	96	prunes	101
Chicken with barbeque		Sima's chicken	100
sauce	99	Spicy baked chicken	99
Lamb kebabs	102	Stir fried chicken and	
Lamb korma with		vegetables	98
bananas	103		

FISH DISHES

Cod provencale	106	Majorcan fish casserole	114
Fish cakes	112	Peppered cod	108
Fish florentine	107	Quick fish casserole	113
Fish parcels	109	Seafood pasta	110
Fish pie	110	Stir fry with prawns	
Fried fish	109	and peaches	107
Grilled fish with		Stuffed baked cod steaks	111
tomato and pesto	108	Tuna, butterbean and	
Kedgeree	112	leek savoury	113
Mackeral in orange and		Tuna and lentil bake	111
ginger	106		

SAUCES

Chick pea + avocado sauce	121	Parsley sauce	118
Curry sauce	121	Pea + caraway sauce	122
Dahl	120	Pesto sauce	118
Fennel + cashew nut sauce	122	Ratatouille sauce	119
French dressing	116	Thousand islands	
Fresh tomato sauce	119	mayonnaise	117
Herb + walnut sauce	119	Tofu mayonnaise	116
Mayonnaise	117	Vegetable puree sauce	120
Mushroom sauce	118	Veloute sauce	118
Onion sauce	118	White sauce	118

BAKING WITHOUT

Almond paste	135	Ginger and orange cake	129
Almond and soya biscuits	132	Mincemeat	136
Apple, date + nut muffins	128	Mince pies	136
Banana, date + nut loaf	128	Onion and herb loaf	131
Carob birthday cake	134	Onion+herb focaccia bread	131
Carob slices	126	Parsnip, banana and	
Carrot and coconut cake	129	apricot slices	125
Chewy fruit bars	133	Popcorn	133
Christmas cake	135	potato flour bread	130
Cornbread	130	Savoury slices	127
Fruit and nut slices	125	Simnel cake	135
		Spiced carrot bread	132

DESSERTS

Almond + mincemeat			
apples	140	Fruit terrine	147
Almond fruit bake	142	Jelly	147
Apricot and banana		Melon + mango sauce	150
cheesecake	138	Prunes and custard	144
Apricot mousse	140	Prune souffle	139
Baked egg custard	145	Rice pudding	141
Baked stuffed apples	141	Spiced pears	150
Banana custard	144	Sponge and custard	144

Banana and mango
ice cream   148
Banana and peach
ice cream   148
Black forest trifle   144
Carob cream   139
Christmas pudding   151
Fried bananas   143
Fresh fruit salad   146
Fruit compote   145
Fruit platter   147

Strawberry and banana
ice cream   148
Strawberry and peach
sorbet   148
Stuffed dates or prunes   151
Stuffed pancakes   149
Stuffed peaches   143
Sweet souffle omelette   149
Vanilla custard   144

NOTES